PIG SQU]

(NEW WRITING SCOTLAND 10)

PIG SQUEALING

(NEW WRITING SCOTLAND 10)

Edited by

JANICE GALLOWAY
and
HAMISH WHYTE

with Meg Bateman (Gaelic Adviser)

Association for Scottish Literary Studies
with support from
Wm Teacher & Sons Ltd
Scotch Whisky Distillers

Association for Scottish Literary Studies
c/o The Department of English, University of Aberdeen
Aberdeen AB9 2UB

First published 1992

ISBN 0–948877–15–4

The Association for Scottish Literary Studies acknowledges
with gratitude subsidy from the Scottish Arts Council
and the support of Wm Teacher & Sons Ltd
in the publication of this volume

Typeset by Roger Booth Associates, Newcastle upon Tyne

Printed by AUP Aberdeen

CONTENTS

INTRODUCTION

Over 500 writers submitted material this year – an embarrass-ment of riches which, considering our limited space and bud-get, meant some severe editing. Simply, there was not space for all we wanted to include. This was frustrating but an excellent discipline for honing down our ideas about what a book like this should try to offer. The final selection is, we hope, a good purseful of things stimulating, remarkable, particular. It was good to see a growing number both of Gaelic submissions and of authors able to refuse to deal with the inverted commas kind of 'Scottishness' and instead examine the old questions in a new way as in A.L. Kennedy's pastiche, 'A Meditation upon Penguins', Irvin Welsh's double-take, 'Where the Debris Meets the Sea' or Ken Cockburn's innocuously-titled 'Kirkaldy. Edinburgh. A Trip Abroad'. Much writing occupied itself with love and its tenuous upkeep – as in the wonderfully comple-mentary pieces from Dilys Rose and Brian McCabe, the acrid aftertaste of John Maley's poetry or the tightly written title-piece from Andrew Cowan.

We are delighted to again present the work of well-known, up-and-coming and brand new writers (including our youngest, Ailish Petrie's dark fairy tale). Despite lingering regret for the excellent pieces which had to be turned away, we think this is a fine volume. Enjoy it.

Janice Galloway
Hamish Whyte
June 1992

NEW WRITING SCOTLAND 11

Submissions are invited for the eleventh annual volume of *New Writing Scotland,* to be published in 1993, from writers resident in Scotland or Scots by birth or upbringing. Poetry, drama, short fiction or other creative prose may be submitted but not full-length plays or novels, though self-contained extracts are acceptable. The work must be neither previously published nor accepted for publication and may be in any of the languages of Scotland.

Submissions should be typed on one side of the paper only and the sheets secured at the top-left corner. Each individual work should be clearly marked with the author's name and address.

Submissions should be accompanied by two stamped addressed envelopes (one for a receipt, the other for return of MSS) and sent by 31 January 1993, to:

Maggie Beveridge, Managing Editor *NWS*
c/o Dept of English Studies
University of Stirling
Stirling FK9 4AL

Donald Adamson

DETACHMENT

Light leaks from the windows
of their portakabin
and soaks into November fog.

Outside there's a grey-out,
inside, a warm fug.
The gas-ring's on.
The hut fills with men
and the yellow flame of waterproofs.
Time for a brew-up; to look ahead
to the weekend, the night out,
the woman ...

For the potency
of digger and drill is on them,
the need vibrates in them.
They'd give their wages for it,
some of them, and will.

But for some there's enough
in a moment-between
of fogbound time, invisible
to the twin gaffers
Work-To-Live
and Life saying *suck my pleasures dry.*

Graham Bell

CONJUGATING T'S AND Q'S

Introduction: 7.30a.m. June 14th.

I moved into this flat approximately 5 months, 3 days, 19 hours ago in the easily deducible icy cold of an early January morning. It contains three rooms, the dimensions of which are as follows:

Bed/Living room	30 x 22 ft
Kitchen	11 x 6 ft
Bathroom	6 x 5 ft

Nothing unusual in that, you might say, although you may wonder at the size of the bathroom. The title is actually a misnomer since obviously no such receptacle could fit into a room of such paltry measurements. In fact, my necessary twice weekly ablutions are carried out in a shower measuring 3 x 3 ft. This space (and indeed that of the whole flat) although ample for my necessities is perhaps rather smaller than my modest ambition might desire.

No, the thing which is unusual about my situation is in fact outwith the flat although not exactly too far away. The intrusive element which provides, shall we say, the 'meat' of my story lives no further than one door away in the shapely form of my neighbour Gloria Winthrope.

I am not, in my humble opinion, a paranoid person but since my arrival she has been round on what seems to me a rather exaggerated number of occasions. To prove my point, I enclose a list of the items which provide the supposed motive for her approximations. Ostensibly 'borrowed', in fact at least half of the items on the list have never been returned. No matter, I recite:

Tea bags	13	(mostly one at a time but on two occasions when 'unexpected guests' arrived she borrowed 3/2 simultaneously)
Coffee	8	these 'units' refer to the occasions
Sugar	16	on which the item in question was
Milk	5	taken since as any grammatician
Washing Powder	1	will tell you these substances are 'uncountable'.

Potatoes	4	
Garlic	2	
Sieve	1	
Screwdriver	2	
Hammer	2	
Total	49	visits

Rather excessive, don't you think? Cogitating on the reasons for these intrusions I came up with three:

(1) The Improbable – she is an agent for the CIA/FBI/MI5/6/ Interpol and is spying on me. Now that I think about it, the toothpaste was in the wrong place two weeks ago and doors have been found open that were closed. The only possible reason for this harassment might lie in my once having belonged to a weird sect with socio-political leanings. Our activities included knitting in nightclubs, holding spiritual togetherness meetings in cinemas and once plotting to write a story about hijacking a national express bus and taking it to London, en route attracting a large convoy of lorries, cars etc. which on arrival at Westminster would overthrow the government.

(2) The Impossible – she is involved with some latter day domestic style Voodoo cult and hopes to steal my soul by hexing my household utensils; since in a (post industrial) materialistic culture (as epitomised in early '90s Glasgow) the true soul of man lies not in his body but in his possessions and most deeply in the most mundane (I guess because the prevailing politico-cultural climate is conformist, dull and definitely GREY). But her spells are useless because I sold my soul to the devil years ago for the power of unlimited memory.

(3) The Likely – she is lonely and trying to establish contact in a world which is cold, alienating and unfriendly.

It would seem logical that there are three ways in which this impasse may be terminated. These are respectively:

(1) She finds my stash of semtex and I end up doing a 'lifer' in Barlinnie.

(2) Her attempts to take me over increase and she asks for hairdryers, food processors and, finally, my microwave. She realises her spells are doing no good and moves out in disgrace.

(3) I go round and invite myself in for a friendly coffee.

Never an overly decisive person, the resolution of my fate I leave to you. The choice is yours, dear reader, the choice is yours.

Pedantry will have calculated that my arithmetic doesn't tally – the number of 'borrowings' [10 (13 - 5 + 2) + 8 + 16 + 5 + 1 + 4 + 2 + 1 + 2 + 2 = 51, not 49]. The reason for this is that the numbers refer to the items in question, and not to the occasion. Twice two items were borrowed simultaneously and therein lies the solution to this apparent anomaly.

Marianne Carey

ONE WAY

Driving along the motorway,
Heading for the second exit after the
Grey corrugated shed with Mr Happy on the side,
A man in a red hatch-back
Drove right up the inside and
He looked so bad-tempered
I lost the place and drove
Straight over the chevrons.
Well that was it.
I couldn't face another motorway slip road
So I just stayed where I was,
In the middle lane doing sixty
Till my petrol ran out,
Two miles north of
Ecclefechan.

A CELEBRATION OF VISION

A thin lady scrawled in red ink
Rose up from the page with her
Carmine nails
And hissed –

You have set my eyes too close.

The round bather dimpled and
Kicked from the canvas, curled her
Pink mouth
And laughed –

You have painted me like a boiled shrimp.

The shadow in the hallway glared
Through chalk, her hands in her
Apron pockets
And groaned –

You have made me look sorry he's gone.

The artist is known particularly for his figure work.
His well-observed studies of women in domestic settings
are especially admired.

THE MOURNING AFTER

You know she told lies,
spiteful.

> What's past, there's no point. Death
> makes bitterness no use.

More tea?
She took what she wanted,
I haven't forgotten

> Remember the good things,
> it's all that seems fair.

The blue organza frock

> There were times she stood up for us,
> at the school trip.

And a man.

> She never tried to be
> The favourite.

She was hard, well
it did her no good.
I'm not sorry.

> You don't mean

If you're not wanting the rest
of that snowball,
I'll have it.

Susan Chaney

ALL THINGS RUDE AND WONDERFUL

I was the only girl who would ever dare to admit to liking the smell of her own farts.

'Blow offs, Sonia,' my mother corrected me reprovingly whenever I used the hated word, 'if you really *must* keep mentioning them, it's so much *nicer* don't you think, to call them blow offs.'

But I was recalcitrant. 'I like "fart" much better. It's on… omat op…oeic…' I dragged the word out – pausing dramatically at the end for full effect.

'What's that mean, Sonia?' asked my younger sister, Jenny – predictable as ever.

I made a raspberry noise between pursed lips. 'It's a word that means the same as it sounds.'

'Like firelight crackling and waves crashing,' my mother added helpfully.

'And fart!' I chimed in from the doorway. Seeing the look on Mum's face I disappeared at high speed, pounding up the stairs two at a time. On the landing I stopped and hung over the banisters.

'Hey Jenny,' I hissed. 'Guess what we're doing in English now? Alliteration. Listen to this. A feebleminded frumpish farter forced her fingers…'

'You just wait till your father gets home, you cheeky little monkey!' my mother shouted up the stairs, but with a catch in her voice that might well be laughter – so I knew it was alright really. You never could tell with Mum – she could go either way.

Later though, as I was sidling about in the corridor with my ears pricked I overheard her talking to Dad in the kitchen.

'You're really going to have to take a much firmer line with that girl, George. She's so *rude* these days, it's unbelievable. You should hear the language she's coming out with! She doesn't learn it here, that's for certain. It's those awful Pender children she's running around with. Little better than juvenile delinquents – the lot of them!'

Creeping closer to peer around the edge of the door I saw my father sitting with his back to me with my mother facing him across the table. Dipping his head to pass his hand over his face, he sighed. I supposed it had been *yet* another long hard day at the office. The days at *his* office were always long and hard. He kept glancing surreptitiously at the evening newspaper lying beside his plate.

'I wouldn't make too much of it, if I were you, Frances. It's harmless. All kids her age love a bit of rudeness. I know I was just the same when I was ten.'

Mum looked at him with exasperated affection. With the uncanny sense of communication I often had with her I could tell that she was thinking that thirty odd years later nothing much had changed.

'*And*' he went on 'She makes you laugh sometimes.'

One hand was already reaching towards the paper, the other toying with the handle of his tea cup.

'Oh well... if *you* think... I suppose...'

'Yes. I do. Better just to ignore her.'

He pushed the cup towards her, adding appealingly. 'Any more tea in the pot dear?'

Disappointed I turned away. There wasn't going to be a scene after all. As long as it didn't get too nasty I quite enjoyed being the cause of a good row. It certainly livened things up a bit.

As well as liking farts I was very fond of sniffing old ladies' bicycle seats.

It was very hot the day Jenny and I watched Miss Beecham ride her new bicycle through the village. Every so often as she pedalled her way up the hill towards the shop she would raise her plump backside and then settle it back more comfortably on her seat. There would be a puff of air and an explosion of rude noises from the tan leather saddle which was still covered by a layer of plastic wrapping. She kept glancing anxiously round hoping no one would think it was her.

She left the bike propped up against the wall. The hot air vibrated around the shiny chrome frame – thick with the smell of plastic and new rubber tyres. Sidling towards it, winking at Jenny over my shoulder, I bent to sniff the seat.

'Ooh good!' I chortled. 'It's *wonderful*! I can smell where her Royal Rudie's been.'

Jenny was something of an amateur when it came to odour. I was the expert – a real connoisseur of olfactory pleasure – an addict even. It was fatal to let me within a hundred yards of a shoe shop. The smell of all that new leather made me go all goggle-eyed and helpless. Other favourites were my pet mice, plastic of all descriptions, the inside of pencil boxes and household cleaners. Once I went too far and got myself completely stoned by sniffing a bottle of Thorpit. It was terrific at first but then I started to feel all sick and wobbly and had to be put to bed. For a few hours I think Mum was really quite worried.

Another rich source of old ladies and their smells was the Village Institute. This was a tiny one-storey ivy-shrouded building, crammed between the church and the vicarage. Mostly it stayed locked and mysterious, but occasionally there would be a coffee morning or a whist drive in aid of the appeal for the repairs to the church roof. Then the folding green baize card tables and the brown canvas chairs would appear from the cupboard. Crisp white cloths, painstakingly embroidered through the winter months, were spread, and on each table a jam jar with a few sweet william and carnations. The ancient tea urn, a relic from Miss Beecham's days with the WRVS, would splutter and hiss in the corner and the thick, white institutional looking cups were filled with dark brown tea.

At one end of the room stood the trestle table with a few crocheted toilet roll holders and dog eared paperback books for sale.

It was best if it was raining – not a real downpour, but a soft summer rain – the kind that beaded the hedgerows and gardens with a fine dew. The damp released the smells of camphor and mothballs from the best coats. The canvas chairs, moistly indented by damp backsides gave off a sad, mouldy kind of scent, like our dog when he'd rolled on a dead sea bird. It was glorious in the village hall on a wet day. The smell of rubber galoshes and dripping umbrellas spiced with the steamy warmth of hot tea and the sweet smell of flowers was completely intoxicating. Sometimes an elderly lady, sinking down with a grateful sigh, would grow careless, and allow her legs to fall open as she bent to unfasten her galoshes. If we were lucky we would catch sight of a pair of knee length celanese interlock knickers!

On wet days in the village hall I could even smell people's armpits from a distance of several yards. It was funny but the vicar never seemed to sweat. His armpits were always as musty and dry as the inside of the tapestry bag he used to take the collection in church. His parishioners, on the other hand, beneath their crepe blouses, eau-de-cologne and lemon grass toilet water, always smelt hot and yeasty with excitement.

Jenny and I always discussed sex on top of the lid of the septic tank at the far end of the garden – the only place where we could be guaranteed some privacy.

'But *how* do you know that "fuck" is something to do with having babies?' Jenny kept asking me. She was adamant that it couldn't be.

'It's just another of those words like "damn" and "bloody hell" that grown ups use when things go wrong, that's all.'

Stalling for time I frowned thoughtfully.

'Damn, Fuck, Bugger.' I said slowly at first – then quicker, savouring the short punchy sound they made.

'Listen to this, Jenny. Damn. Fuck. Bugger. There're onomatopoeic!'

But Jenny wasn't so easily diverted.

'How can they be? You said that was words that sound the same as they mean.'

'Well it is.'

'But, we *don't* know what they mean, do we? That's the trouble isn't it?'

For once I was at a loss for words. It was all too difficult. When I showed Jimmy Pender my white mice struggling together in the straw he said 'fuck' in a tone of awed authority. Dad, on the other hand, when he hit his thumb with the hammer said the same word in a completely different way altogether.

Another area of confusion was between the words 'Durex' and 'Tampax'. We argued furiously back and forth about this for ages. Were they or weren't they used for the same purpose?

'And is it true,' she asked, 'that a lady can get a baby just by sitting on a man's lap?'

And 'Sonia, do boys get monthlies too?'

'I'm not sure, but I don't think so.'

I didn't really know what monthlies were except that mum got them and they involved blood, lots of trips to the toilet and being cross.

Jenny looked up at me pleadingly – needing me to be

certain. I sighed. Sometimes the weight of my responsibility towards her was a burden I could do without. Falling back upon my air of insouciant bravado, I said airily,

'Oh no. Of *course* they don't. Just think how awful it would be when they went to the toilet – all the blood would come spurting out of their willies!'

We were obsessed by bums and armpits: fascinated by the way people smelt and what they had between their legs. We were constantly alert; always watching, always waiting.

The first time I saw Dad's penis I was hidden up the laburnum tree in the back garden. It was a windy day in early May and the sky was rocking with brilliant yellow laburnum and pink and white flowering cherry. I was having to grip tight to keep my balance in the tree. My hands and knees were scraped and smeared with green from the branches.

With a small grunt he flung down his spade and crossed the garden towards me, unbuttoning his flies as he walked. In my excitement I almost fell out of the tree. I had never seen a man's before. The boys in the village were always taking theirs out and waving them around – once William Nankervis had chased me across the cliffs with his – but this was very different. It was much bigger. Much. And a different colour.

The arc of his pee was a deep yellow. When he'd finished he shook it carefully, swearing to himself when a few drops splashed over his wellingtons.

Was it *really* true that if a man or boy peed against an electric fence they'd get electrocuted? But then why would anyone want to pee against an electric fence in the first place? Or in empty milk bottles, the backyard or the kitchen sink? My father's habits infuriated my mother.

'Why *can't* you go up and use the toilet, George?' she was always asking.

Once when he came in from peeing in the garden she said,

'You men are all the same. I've yet to meet one who had the decency to use the proper place. Is it laziness or what?'

Banging the tea pot down on the table, she turned and glared at him.

'It seems to me it's just like dogs marking out their territory.' She snorted scornfully. 'Immature and insecure the lot of you. Little boys that never grow up!'

This was going a bit too far. 'At least he's not as bad as Paul next door,' I protested. 'He's been caught using the chip pan and his gum boots!'

On summer days I would watch my father strip to the waist in the garden – his nakedness, an alien landscape, growing familiar. The skin on his chest was very white – girlish almost – at his neck a vee of reddish sunburn – his forearms stained to the elbow. The tight brown knots of his nipples sprouted a few wiry brown hairs. A line of darker hair ran from his shallow navel into the waistband of his trousers. Making some excuse to get closer to him I smelled his fresh sweat – tangy, raw, yet somehow sweet. Usually he wore a suit and smelled of dark cloth, newly laundered shirts and Old Spice shaving soap.

Dad could be good fun and seemed to enjoy farts and things like that as much as we did. In the mornings at breakfast he would lift one buttock off his chair and fart loudly – announcing with relish. 'Ahh, that's better!' – making us giggle into our cornflakes.

Cutting her toast into smaller and smaller squares Mum would always frown and sigh despairingly.

'George, for goodness sake! *Must* you be so crude? These girls are bad enough already without you carrying on like that.'

But she spoke with resignation – with the air of one who was already defeated. Her self-imposed role of guardian of our moral standards was a hopeless one.

Dad, winking at us over the edge of the morning paper invariably replied,

'Hold your wind and bear the pain.

Let it rip and bear the shame.'

Mum would get up crossly and start clattering the plates about in the sink. Following her he would catch her from behind and swing her off her feet while she beat ineffectually at his head with the dishcloth.

'It's no good, Frances. You can't really expect us to take you seriously. You're just too small!'

By this time we were on our feet too, egging him on – waiting for her to start laughing – because she always did in the end.

Eventually he put her down. Flushed and breathless she leant back against the cooker, straightening her skirt, patting her hair into place. Sometimes the laughter stopped abruptly

and I would catch her looking at me – a long troubled look –
almost as if she were warning me. But then she was *always*
warning us of something or other. Somedays she started every
other sentence with the words 'Now look, I'm warning you...'
and if we had to go to the toilet when out shopping in the
town she would never let us sit on the seat in public lavatories
in case we caught some nameless disease. When pressed for
more details as to the exact nature of this disease she would
only purse her lips, shake her head and say, darkly enigmatic,
'You can never be too careful. Just you remember that,
you girls.'
She was like that – never specific. So for a long time I
didn't take much notice.

There were no fitted carpets or central heating in our house
and on winter mornings I watched my mother as she hobbled
over the stained wood floorboards from her bed to the ward-
robe, complaining bitterly about the cold. She walked on her
heels with her toes turned out – reminding me of snails – the
way they moved sometimes with their bodies reared upwards.
Until I was about twelve and a half seeing her feet like this, vul-
nerable, blue with cold, swollen with chilblains, was the most
intimate I had been with her.
Everyone else was fair game, but *not* my mother. My
mother's body was forbidden territory – strictly taboo. Then
one day she forgot to lock the bathroom door. Desperate for
the toilet I came hurtling along the landing and burst into the
bathroom. Seeing by mother in the bath through a fog of
steam I stopped dead and stared at her. She was *very* small –
smaller even than I'd thought and her skin was all wrinkled. I
was shocked and outraged. It was worse than coming home
from school to find the telly not working or the tea uncooked.
I couldn't understand it either. She wasn't all *that* old and her
face wasn't wrinkled; it was still quite smooth and pretty. Her
tummy was saggy and scored with a mass of fine white lines.
Hanging on her chest were a pair of tiny shrivelled breasts –
horribly similar to those of African women I'd seen and
laughed over on the travelogue programmes. Her expression
was puzzling – sort of sad but ordinary – like when her purse
was empty by Thursday and the housekeeping didn't come till
Friday. She beckoned me forwards until I was standing right
beside the bath. Through my tartan pleated skirt I could feel

the porcelain rim of cool against my leg. She looked at me a long time before nodding slowly. I backed away. As if reading my thoughts she looked down at her stomach, resignedly flicking at one of her nipples.

'This is what happens to a woman's body,' she said, 'when she has two children and feeds them herself.'

I was barely back outside the door when Jenny came rushing up the stairs, her face all white and tearful.

'Come on. Come on! You've got to come quick. It's horrible! The mice have eaten all their babies!'

The overcrowded mice had turned on the latest litter tearing them to pieces. Many of them weren't yet dead. We stood in silence staring down at the tangle of hairless mutilated little bodies. The bloodstained straw smelt horrible.

My face clenched with determination until my jaw ached.

'We'll *have* to kill them. We can't leave them like that.'

'No! I couldn't,' wailed Jenny, 'I'm scared. Can't we wait till Daddy comes home?'

I pressed a heavy stone into her hand so hard it almost made her cry.

'No. It's too long. They're suffering.'

Lifting my own rock above the cage, I heard my voice rising painfully. 'They're suffering. And it's all my fault.'

I closed my eyes and shouted. 'Hit them, Jenny. Go on! Hit them as hard as you can.'

My stone slammed down. A moment later Jenny's followed. Once. Twice.

'Again, Jenny. Again!'

The tears were pouring down my burning face, my arm pumped the stone desperately up and down. I tried not to hear the awful muffled thud it was making. Tried not to see my mother's body – the way her feet dangled helplessly when my father lifted her up. It seemed to go on forever. In the blurry darkness I was blind and lost.

Dimly I heard Jenny's terrified cry. 'Stop it, Sonia! *Please.* They're all dead now. I can see them.'

Flinging down the stone, I leaned against the wall. Jenny was staring at me as if I were a stranger – her hands clutched protectively across her chest.

I couldn't bear it, that she should look at me like that. I stumbled towards her, needing her innocent warmth again –

her unquestioning love. I sobbed against her jumper.

There was a long, cold, terrible moment then slowly her arms came round me.

Maggie Christie

THE MUSIC CAME THROUGH

The big smoothie man
With the big smoothie hi-fi
Wanting to use its power
Over you and me together
(*Harmless, you know, with two of them there*)
When I wanted to be with you

The big smoothie man
Said Beethoven was better on good equipment
But to me the music came through
On the school's machine,
Scratches and all, in the dining hall,
When the teacher left me alone with you.
Perhaps she knew.

And the music came through
In the practice cells, in the gaps between classes,
The cracks of time, the strain of score-reading
Lightened by playing together –
Symphonies could be duets, duets symphonic.

The big smoothie man
Trying for heroics with fancy machines
Can have the funeral march;
We'll take off with the false return
And the scherzo.
We'll have a trio with our music teacher –
Eroica – the feminine ending.

Barbara Clarke

STARS IN THE BLACK WATER

No-one would have believed that the woman who had knelt over the hip bath stirring custard for the communion break-fast for little Joel the same day her waters broke with her ninth child, would be sitting on the railway track some two years later with a white cloth and cheese sandwiches laid out like the harvest picnic, not flinching at the sight of the 9.45a.m. Scots Princess trembling towards her in a deathly rage, and she sitting with her head cocked on one side as though she were listening to spring birds.

Bridget had gold hair and an almond complexion, a pink sugared almond. She got up before first light and went to bed long after the moon sat menacing in the sky. She had no time for 'high jinks' as she would call them, the busybody fussy women who came in coarse tweed suits and velvet hats, flaunt-ing their corseted bodies over her best furniture which they had the audacity to sweep with their hands, flicking them as if they were covered with invisible insects before sitting down; perching on the edge as if they wouldn't be staying long.

But they did and the 'Sister' from the parish would nod and keep her eyes fixed on the other women, saying 'that's right Bridget' in answer to the woman's admonishments.

Bridget would carry on with the ironing, licking her fingers and patting her hair so it stopped from falling in front of her eyes. Sometimes she would forget to cover up her milk stained blouse or to put on her shoes to hide her rough bunioned feet; she would lose her confidence for a moment and not be able to fix the woman with her dark treacle stare.

The nun would pale as the woman said, 'Perhaps she should move her bed in with the girls now they were older, let the boys sleep with their father instead, it would save so many problems in the future. Hadn't she, Bridget, got her hands full now with the new one just come?' Bridget would feel her face redden but keep on ironing the dampened clothes.

After they had gone she would sit by the stove, with the door to the scullery closed. She would cry a little and think of that evening by the harbour where the Christmas lights danced, reflecting in the black water like stars. She a woman

with so much to do. A life ahead full of promises of going on
the boats, not to trawl the fish and spend her days with
ragged blistered hands from gutting herring, and tying knots
in holed nets, but to get away from all of them; the old
women in their black shawls shuffling round the houses like
beetles, all of them, whispering their nonsense, holding rosary
beads pretending they were praying to the lamb of god, the
innocent lamb awaiting the slaughter.

But that night by the harbour she was sheltering in the
innocent embrace of Kenny and in the summer she was rocking the child, her first born, who may as well have been born
in a manger.

She wept thinking about the arms of Kenny, that woman
must be mad to ask her to move her bed willingly from next
to his, where night shadowed death, where his beer-stained
mouth caught hers like evening moths on the flowers which
sat full and yellow round her mother's grave; where she could
feel her skin warm against his, where she could for a few
moments not have to think about making ham bones into
soup, enough to last the week.

It was getting light in the evenings, she didn't have to wrap
herself in Kenny's old army coat to go down to the privy at the
bottom of the garden. She had tried her best to grow roses so
they grew up and hung over, disguising the reality of life. She
always imagined a garden with roses clambering up the walls,
full with velvet promises, soft pink and so delicate to smell.
But the earth was dead and the privy was a damp earth closet,
where a nest of five rats was found by one of her screaming
boys. Kenny buried them alive, trod the earth harder and
harder, their muffled eerie squeals gradually fading. The privy
had a few slats of wood which hung as a door; Bridget would
wait until dark before she would escape in peace, to be alone
in private.

Kenny asked her, 'Where do you pee in the day?' He was
dealing out the cards, was all dressed up in his new shirt and
cardigan, there were some friends of his from work, years ago
when they all had jobs. They came every few weeks with cans
of beer, tightly fitting into the kitchen. This time he had
warned her so that when the singing started and Kenny or
one of the others fell off their chair there was no child under
the table making a house or playing boats threatening to have
their hands trodden on, there was no dog to start yelping,

snapping at their ankles, and no children banging the same five out of tune keys on the piano. She had kept the children quiet, their mouths stuck together with treacle toffee and lemonade made fizzy with bicarbonate of soda. They promised to stay away, promised each other they wouldn't be the cause of another bruise on their mother's face.

Bridget had washed her hair, ironed her dress and put cream on her face, made an effort to smile as Kenny came in the house. She offered him her eyes, offered him herself, and she breathed softly like cats asleep on the old man's knees. She was stirring the turnips and getting the pies hot in the oven, the cups were ready for tea and he'd said it just like he had asked was there more sugar. At first she thought she must be imagining it, a question like that, so she carried on mashing the potatoes, and the men laughed, softly at first, then louder. She stood frozen for a moment with her back to them but she could feel him staring and then she could smell his breath, the stale breath, his large hands firm on her hips and he said it again and again.

'Where do you pee in the day, you're not shy are you, you don't think you're better than us, Bridget high and mighty waits till dark to pull down her drawers' and on and on he went, the others laughing, dealing out the cards.

With the coming of spring Bridget would spend the late evenings reading. Her uncle had taught her to read.

'It was an accident' he said, he hadn't meant anything by it, she reminded him so much of Kathleen. Bridget didn't understand what he meant, as Kathleen his girlfriend had black hair scraped back from her lined fleshy face.

Bridget had been burying her dolls by the compost where the goldfish were put when they died. She had made them proper coffins out of shoe boxes and had bits of cloth for shrouds. He had come along the path behind the garden sheds and said, 'What's that you're doing?' She told him she was burying her dolls and he'd laughed and sucked on his pipe and said, 'So you're too big to play with dolls', and then he was there behind her, touching her neck with his hand, sliding over her dress, her lovely dress with hats and dancing soldiers and he touched her leg, her thigh and her new soft breasts.

Afterwards lying on the grass he blew tobacco smoke so it spiralled, and Bridget looked at him and said, 'Billy would you teach me to read?'

He didn't say anything for a long time, and then softly broke into a laugh and said, 'I'll teach you to read, but we must find a quiet place where we won't be disturbed, find a secret place where just you and I can go.'

On Saturday afternoon he would come with his fishing rod and magazine, a rug to sit on and sometimes he would share his orange and chocolate and sometimes he wouldn't. He'd say, 'Let the sun brown you Bridget.' Bridget would sit burning while he read her stories, showed her the letters that spelled her name and then he'd close the book and pull her close to his wet mouth.

When the children had come she had worked hard. She cried when the first one stirred but then felt warmth and hope and crying again, pushed them out onto the well-worn bed. She would sometimes lie for a few days or a week, all her senses blunted, while her neighbours bathed and fed the children, cooked and cleaned the stove for Kenny. While she birthed, Kenny would be out of the way in the pub until it was all over, from the first cry to the last and sometimes that was two days; once he had been delivered himself in a cart pulled by an aged mule by the old farmer living over the hill.

Bridget had not been herself, Lilly from down the road had told the priest who quietly smiled to himself, nibbling the wild cherry tarts and apple pies his faithful women brought him, usually on a Friday, the day before confession.

The priest had visited Bridget in the morning, he'd stood in the rain peering through the smeared windows. She had seen him but carried on sweeping the floor. He had come in uninvited and put his hat on the table, he was a young man new to the village, a young man too blue eyed to be a priest. Inside the house he had been unsure where to sit, unsure of his place. She had put down the pot of tea, the large black pot and the best cup and saucer. Above them the ceiling seemed it might give way under the rolls and thumps of the tumbling children, but she ignored it and the priest cowered. She laughed quietly as he fumbled for questions and she sat, arms leaning on her knees smoking. She could feel her breasts hanging freely under her shirt, wondered whether her nipples would show through the thin cotton. She thought about the priest, such a young man to counsel her. She sipped tea and said, 'Would you bury a rapist Father?' She said it in a low voice, staring out of the bleary window. The priest stopped sipping his tea; the cup rattled in its saucer as he let it down clumsily. Bridget went on, 'You see, I always thought it was funny that you can murder someone, you can rape you own mother and be buried, but not if you take your own life.'

Bridget stubbed out the cigarette and bent down to pick up the colander of apples. They were fat apples but bruised from falling. She peeled them slowly while the priest watched her silently.

It was Whitsuntide, the time of the church picnic. The children had been arranged in clean skirts and shirts and had jars filled with honey water and paper bags filled with bread and dripping, and each of them had a slab of cherry cake. Kenny had gone with them part of the way and then gone on to play bowls, taking his fishing rod should he get bored.

Bridget packed her basket, her grandmother's tablecloth left from her wedding. She pulled out the bath and lit the stove to boil up some water. Firstly she uncoiled her hair, combing it with lavender oil, then slipped down into the water, letting it spill over the edge, her legs heavy and fat filling most of the bath. Afterwards she dried herself and sprinkled fine musk rose powder between her breasts and over her stomach and put on her newest blouse.

There was time to take the path down past the river, moments to stand watching the fish tangle in the weeds. She was ready with her hat and coat, her picnic basket full of cheese and fruit. Bridget closed the door thinking of the train and the poems she had copied into her notebook, small verses that had kept her lips silent when so badly she had wanted to cry out, to call out to make life stop. She held the book tight, the small shabby cover wrapped in an old silk cloth, each page with a pressed leaf or petal the fragrance and colour crushed out long ago; flowers trapped a short memory of good times sitting in the sun, playing with a child, learning new dances, tasting wine for the first time.

Ken Cockburn

KIRKCALDY. EDINBURGH. A TRIP ABROAD

Three men in a van, taking a show out on the road. At a petrol station, two of us stealing money from a local yokel's wallet which stupidly he's left in his van, driving away before he notices in a wide, wide arc across the forecourt. I'm on a seat attached to the outside of the driver's seat, no door between us, so I decide I'd rather walk. The driver thinks I'm daft.

Arriving in Birmingham I do some sight-seeing but there's not much to see. I find a gloomy museum, all net curtains and huge, heavy, display cabinets. I run out of staircases to go down but come across a lift. I call it and climb up the two or three steps in. Inside it's roomy and luxurious, mirrored smoked-glass walls, inviting low armchairs, tables set with bowls of cocktail nibbles. The doors are about to close when there's a rush of people. Someone presses a button for the top floor, although I want to go as low as possible, because of my vertigo.

I walk out onto a narrow, dusty street, and take the train to Kirkcaldy. The train itself is busy and smoky, but the journey includes a pleasant stroll along a sunny footpath beneath the Forth Railway Bridge. At each station I take cuttings of plants that are growing on the platform. Then I think I've arrived and get off the train, but it turns out to be the wrong station, a new one called 'Kirkeby'. The guard claps shut a metal device and I turn round to see the train shoot off into the tunnel. There are no timetables to say when the next train leaves, just notices and adverts, and the ticket collector has joined the other staff behind a market stall further along the platform. Among the displays, long-haired girls are dancing languidly to Spanish music. I can see Kirkcaldy at the foot of the hill, bright, grey-stone buildings above a sparkling sea. I wonder what the French Assistante makes of it. I start to make my way down, but my feet are tired and I'm wearing the brown DMs I don't like walking in. Seafield Tower looms out of the twilight.

The town. At a window overlooking the Beveridge Park pond, were we admiring the ships or was it the swans? The

War Memorial Gardens, in front of the Library, the book-shelves among the trees, and above the trees the librarians, in the library proper. Or a street, bungalows set back from the road, where I glimpse a red-haired boy who's not Jim, as I've just seen Jim elsewhere. I run through the crowds after him, and persuade him to come down Milton Road with me. The house on the corner has a large garden with a dead hedge cut in the shape of a football goalpost, that stretches into the street. I try to push the two sides together like a concertina. The whole thing collapses. I lose James when he goes along Links Street to the football, even though I've told him there's no match today, it was yesterday, Raith v Stirling Albion. I think it was a draw.

I look in at the theatre on the way to my parents. The building is a ramshackle collection of old classrooms, with worn wooden floors and a musty smell. Some people from Spectacle Theatre in the Rhondda are there so I say hello, no-one I actually knew, but we seem to be friends. There's a Tennessee Williams play on, about a poor black taxi driver who drives with his glasses chained to a plank of wood, so no-one can steal them. He knows he can't afford a new pair. One day he picks up the Devil, a quiet, middle-aged gent with grey-ing hair and a greying, pointed beard. The taxi driver pulls his car, a dirty, dark-blue Volvo 244, over to the side, and punc-tures a tyre. These things happen when you get a surprise.

It's been a difficult journey, so I lie down on an old metal-framed bed and fall asleep. I dream about waking up and trying to remember what I dreamt, but fall asleep in the pro-cess. When I wake up it's late, already 10, and I should have been with my parents by 7. I reckon I ought to buy my sister a present.

On the High Street I buy two ice-cream cones. After a while I eat one, which still hasn't melted, but I'm not sure how long the other will keep. In a department store, I crouch to look at the stock beneath the pen counter. Plenty ink (£99 for 10 boxes) but I don't see any pens. I go into John Menzies to buy a newspaper, and meet two friends whose flat I'm in. We decide to go out for a drink. I'm concerned as I've just passed a huge queue outside the ABC, waiting for the late-night showing of something Argentinean, but the pub's a bit beyond this, so should be OK. We go into the concourse of the shopping centre, where boys are throwing themselves around like balls. Fights develop. I'm at one end and want to get to the other. I think, if I walk straight on I won't get involved. I get involved. It's Saturday night. Where should I say I've been? The name Cree's Inn springs to mind. Have I been there recently enough to be able to fool them?

Walking away along a dark track, the Aberdeen football team catch up with me. I sit on the ground with a pint and they gather round, a forest of legs. One of them sneaks off down a path through the undergrowth, but I see him and shout not to, it doesn't go anywhere. My parents drive off in a car.

Walking on, the light of a long summer evening through the trees, dappling a mossy drystane wall. I haven't done this for ages. But it means I have to walk all the way to Edinburgh, and while I've done it before often enough, my feet are sore and I'm only wearing my slippers. At Inverkeithing I come across an advertising display, made up of ceramic tiles, for the Ian Hamilton Finlay exhibition I've been working on. The exhibition is over, but I think the tiles should be kept, as they might become valuable. Taking down the display, I'm pleasantly surprised by the variety and erudition of the tiles. I put these, along with slides and other bits and pieces which are lying on the ground, into a plastic shoulder bag which belongs to an actor, so I have to extend the shoulder strap. I think about the trek still to come, across the Forth Road Bridge and the ten miles of motorway to Edinburgh. In my flat there, I change into my walking boots. I'm about to continue the journey when I think, no, I'm already here, I might as well stay. It takes me a while to make up my mind, but eventually, that's what I decide to do.

In the Talbot Alpine, I become aware I've been reversing at 40 m.p.h. for some time. People I meet are treating me as an Indian factory owner, but what I can't understand is why an Indian factory owner would drive a tatty old Talbot. In the factory canteen I meet three people, including one played by Julie Walters. I sit down to read. Rosie from Spectacle Theatre asks what the book is, and it turns out it's the one about the Indian factory owner!

It's just a dream of course, and I wake up in the flat at Willowbrae, where I'm sharing the bedroom with my ex-flatmate Dave, who stays when Tamsin, my wife, isn't here. I notice he's redecorated the whole room in a deep red, the colour of my Moroccan carpet. Curtains, walls, ceiling and floor, the lot.

As I'm about to be married, we crack open a few cans of beer. I go upstairs to the shower-room to change. Inside is a big man with a greatcoat. He inspires such loyalty for the quality of his, I don't catch the word. He sings as well. I'm dancing, as everyone is, including Chris, who's recently returned, wearing his fawn raincoat. Somebody comments on how mature he looks, saying, 'you would trust him, he looks good on TV.' Dancing, everything's very held in. I mock this a moment, sending out knees and elbows everywhere. Others do too and we twist away for a moment.

I go to look at another flat nearby, pleased it's in such a nice location. No-one else is there to see it, and I only notice the landlord, a Mr B., when he speaks. He's a small, very dark-skinned Indian man, with a green scarf over his head. He shows me in. On the floor we find hard, shrivelled pieces of food, or tacks. A cat's there too. We wonder if it'll eat any of these things, so the landlord lights one of the gas rings. The cat's not interested. As the pan of water's still bubbling on the ring, I make an onion sauce I've just read the recipe for, then mumble something about letting him know.

Steep streets in the Dean Village, darkness, or twilight. I go into a pub, which is like an old-fashioned café, bright lights and formica-topped tables. I order a pint of beer. It tastes lovely. I drink it slowly, savouring it. As I make my way to the theatre, I think the play will probably be over. The foyer is steep but very plush, a balcony topping a wide, red-carpeted staircase with heavy wooden banisters. There's an Alan Spence play on, about the Old Town. I should have been there by 8.30, and it's already 10, but I'm told it'll go on till 2. On a bright, sparse stage, a few people move about in a strange way, speaking strangely too. Perhaps it's Old Scots. I'm pleased I can still see it, though annoyed it lasts so long.

I hear the theatre has appointed an English soprano. She has more or less the house sound, but her technique is astonishing. My first sight of her is in a Highland setting, behind steamed-up glass in a lean-to. Her long blonde hair, a long, blue-green dress, chickens all around her. Other people are preparing a garden, planting coriander and mint, and using old palettes to build a platform for the elephants. Someone makes an impassioned speech about how the elephants have become shadows of their former selves. One in particular is now a 'Highland dolphin', driven mad by the cold and wandering for miles.

For the finale, everyone is costumed for 'The Crucible' and stands in a line. Jessica, a dancer and the only woman on stage, begins the song, contorting her mouth into grotesque shapes but making beautiful sounds. Then someone else sings too, and then I'm counted in. I don't know the song and try to copy the actor next to me, but this is impossible. The music is haunting and soft. Afterwards the other actors congratulate me on my performance. 'Last night the song, tonight the character!' says one.

Outside it's still light, early evening, August, the Festival. I go out and come in again several times, thinking I might go for a drink with the actors, but they drift away, until only one of them is left, and the board for the wine bar has been taken away.

Outside it's a sunny evening on Melville Street. A group of people at the bus stop are lamenting the fact that Julie Walters has just left the theatre she's been working for, possibly been sacked. They saw her as the last hope for the writers' theatre, and now she's gone. Julie is just coming out from L'Attaché, and we walk down Melville Street together. She gets more and more upset, and I comfort her. We cuddle. Soon we're lying on the pavement, kissing. I ask her what's making her so unhappy, and she says, 'my breasts'. I put my hand over one of them, from beneath.

I have to take the bus home but I'm at Haymarket, so I walk to the end of Princes Street where I've a better chance of catching one. It starts drizzling. I'm conscious all the time of wearing trousers, when I should be in the kilt by now. To get on to Princes Street I have to negotiate some windy streets and a small, narrow hump-backed bridge over a stream by the beach. This is very tricky, as large coaches, almost its full width, are squeezing across it.

I walk down behind the station to Market Street, where a new bookshop has opened up. My father hasn't bought anything yet, but notices a boat or a bi-plane hanging from the ceiling. He starts to ask the assistant how much it costs, but doesn't, meandering on and on without getting to the point. Passing the bookshop later, I see a clock reading 10 to 7, and a sign reading 'Open till 7', and hear noise inside, but all the boards have gone. At the top of Easter Road lots of buses pass which I can't get, a 20, a 37, and so on. Eventually I get on one that's sitting at the stop. It promptly does a U-turn and hurtles all the way back to the centre of town.

At Greyfriars a group of East German soldiers leaps off a tram and dives into a glass-fronted shop. They're wanting to go back for the Revolution, I explain to Will. We stroll through the strife-torn city and come to a friend's flat. I lounge at a window with a view of the castle cliff, ordering a pile of letters into the German and Russian ones. A boy on a ladder taps the window from outside, and asks us to open it so he can come in. He's climbed a long way, but we can't be bothered, and tell him to go to the next window down. He says instead he'll keep climbing.

Downstairs it's stopped raining and there are more wooden buildings. I meet Alan, who I'd expected to be in Cyprus. We talk about the play 'The Physicists', which he's directing, but the old classroom we're in soon fills up, and when the teacher arrives, we leave. I raise the problem of the three doors, but Alan has a more important matter on his mind.

I decide to take a little trip.

In Paris, at the Trocadero Metro station, someone swims through the Metro caverns in record time. Tamsin's black cat, Pip, jumps from my high hotel-room window into a pool below, and swims to another balcony, where the water laps. I think, nothing can live in that water, then notice a single, brown fish, with a downward-facing sucker mouth. Slowly the pool fills up with all sorts of fish and animals including, finally, a crocodile.

In Switzerland, a night bus full of African 'Gastarbeiter' passes a huge, illuminated mountain, so steep at the top it's vertical. A day-time stop in a town on a lake, at night I have to run to catch the bus again, hindered by a bulky object I'm carrying. All the mountains look so beautiful in the dark.

In Greece, near an old coastal temple, Will and I are pushing bicycles along the top of a high wall. Then we push them over the edge. Will jumps down into the sea below and I follow him, but the wall is sloped and becomes steps we descend to the bottom of a dank tower. We sit in a wall-recess which once housed a great statue of Jupiter. Lots of little frogs squat by a wooden door, as a huge frog croaks from the opposite corner. It emerges and eats greedily one of the smaller ones.

In Athens, crowds are celebrating by the river. As I walk across a busy park, an Englishman joins me. He says my name twice, the first time enquiringly, the second time more definitely although, not knowing him, I haven't responded. He tells me he's come to Athens to make rolls, and shows me a white U-shaped roll that's been cut in half. 'People are buying them,' he says, 'but I feel terrible, because they're replacing the wonderful old Greek bread, full of meat and onions.'

In Turkey, Will introduces me to many people, both Turkish and Western. It's a time of rapid change. Things that were frowned upon as unacceptable two years ago are now done openly in the street. Sheep, or plants, are laid out on a beach all day when they're killed, to ease the pain of their dying. On the beach with my parents, we come across a huge shoe, with a piece of bone attached to the heel, and a claw at the toe. My mother compares it to her own shoes. It's longer, and over twice the width. Does it belong to a dinosaur or has an artist made it? I look it up in the catalogue and read out, with a great sense of discovery, 'Yves Tanguy, page seventy-three'.

In Romania, Paul and I are given a lift by a woman in a purple mini, with 'Maxim Transit' written on the side. She speaks good English, but attacks Paul with a broken key. He fights back, the key falls, she manages to retrieve it and cuts a vertical line down through her eye and cheek. The car, out of control, veers off the road down a dusty, barren track, and crashes into a rock. A grey Romanian AA van arrives to help us. The back doors of the van have no windows and are very thick, and as we climb in, I look round. Pursuing us is the car of Eva Braun, but she stops to ask someone the way and the van drives off. Back at Paul's house in Murrayfield, I take one last look down the hill. The road is empty. I look for my guitar, in Paul's dark-room, but fall asleep. When I wake up there are two cats beside me, and an old brown-and-white dog.

Sleepily I go through to the kitchen. Pale morning sunshine comes through an opaque window, and a boy is sitting on the fridge, giving examples to do with Neustettin. In an adjoining room there are seven or eight Russian students. This morning there was a speech from one of the leaders about the falseness of the use of Marxist-Leninist doctrine in the running of the country, and this group has come to declare their roubles. The first one takes a long time to hand them over, and someone asks to come back later. I excuse myself, saying my presence isn't really necessary. The official professor, in his mid-30s, bulky, moustached, and wearing a light suit, becomes very angry. Will and I want some lemonade but, because of the Revolution, the grocers will be shut. The turmoil in the room behind me grows as it darkens outside.

Neil Cooper

'I'M NOT YOUR FUCKING MOTHER'

Alan was finding stamping out a cigarette increasingly difficult. Then again, he was willing to admit it could've been the beer. The problem was his right shoe. He normally stamped out cigarettes with his right foot, but at the moment there was a hole in his right shoe. So every time he finished a cigarette he had to remember to stamp it out with his left shoe, which didn't quite have a hole in it yet. This left him off balance, especially after what he'd had to drink.

There was nothing he could do. Shoes were so expensive.

He'd have to walk home tonight though. And in truth he was putting off going home. He thought of Carol, lying there awake, waiting for him.

He dropped a cigarette, stamped it out with his left foot, then scratched his right foot with the heel of his left shoe.

It was always the same.

'Alan?' Carol would say as he fumbled beneath the covers.

'What?' he'd answer, and she'd pause for effect.

'You stink of booze,' is what she'd say.

'Oh,' he'd answer, then pretend to sleep.

They'd lie silent for a while, avoiding one another's bodies. Then if he wasn't really asleep by then they'd usually argue and make up, then maybe make love before they fell asleep wrapped inside each other.

It was always the same.

But what could he do? He liked to drink. She didn't. It was that simple. So why all the angst?

It was closing time now. He drank up and tossed his last cigarette to the floor, remembering to stamp it out with his left shoe, the one without the hole. He didn't have change for the cigarette machine. He'd get another pack in the morning.

The house was silent. Alan closed the door behind him noisier than he intended. He was drunk and in considerable discomfort. He pulled off his shoes in the hall outside their bedroom. He stumbled with the effort, and the shoes fell heavy onto bare floorboards.

Alan stood motionless a moment, but it was too late. A

light had been switched on in the bedroom. Alan looked down at his feet. He looked at his right foot in particular. The sock was sodden and grimy.

The bedroom door swung open. Carol stormed out without looking at him. Alan went to say something, but she was already in the bathroom. Alan peeled off his socks and stood on the cold boards. His right foot was itchy. He scratched it till it hurt but it made no difference. The top of his foot was red and enflamed. He picked up a shoe and sniffed it.

The bathroom door opened. Alan held out the shoe for Carol, blocking her path. He grinned.

'I need new shoes,' he said.

'I'm not your fucking mother,' she said, and slammed the bedroom door behind her.

In bed Carol studiously avoided his touch. She may as well be in another country for all she gives me, thought Alan. He couldn't sleep. His foot was itchy. Worse, it was sore, but he daren't scratch it in case it hurt all the more. That was the real agony.

He turned onto his back, then onto his side, then over onto his front, and then onto his other side.

'What's wrong with you?' he heard her say.

'Wrong?' he said. 'What do you mean, what's wrong?'

Answering a question with another question was a ploy they both knew well.

Alan heard Carol breathing through the silence.

'Forget it,' she said. He didn't.

After a while of no-one saying anything he said, 'My feet itch. I need new shoes.'

'Don't drink so much then.'

He pondered the logic of this, then shifted his body towards her.

'Carol?'

'Go away. You stink.'

He moved his hand across her hips, resting it on her belly. He kissed her shoulder. She put her hand over his, squeezing it a little. He nestled into her and closed his eyes.

He was all set to say he was sorry when he couldn't fight it any longer. Wrenching himself from Carol, Alan put his left foot on top of his right and scratched with all his might for what felt like ages. He did the same with the other foot, just to even things up a little.

'What is it?' asked Carol.

'I need new shoes,' he said. 'My feet are in agony.' His words were slurred. Carol sighed.

'I'll get you some cream to rub on tomorrow,' she said.

'I need new shoes,' Alan said again, louder this time. But she was already asleep.

He lay awake for hours, turning this way and that, scratching occasionally, dying for a cigarette.

Andrew Cowan

PIG SQUEALING

It was the pig that woke my grandfather on the morning Gran died. It was squealing outside in the garden. The noise didn't wake him at once but crept into his sleep and brought on a dream. He dreamt he was back home in Glasgow, in the slaughterhouse where he first worked beside Gran. They were children then, barely into their teens, but in his dream they were already old, shrunken and wrinkled, twice the age of their parents. Grandad was trying to butcher a pig. He struck it repeatedly on the back of its skull with a mawl, but the animal was stubborn and refused to buckle beneath him. All the while it was squealing. Gran was squatting by a tub of scalding hot water, ready to scrape it, patiently waiting, and in the shadows behind her their parents were watching, huddled together and whispering. Grandad began to sweat as freely as the blood that flowed from the pig, until he could hardly see what he was doing. 'There's nae strength in me, Agnes,' he said. But Gran didn't respond. She dipped her elbow in the water and smiled to the parents, who cooed and muttered admiringly. He continued to strike at the pig, crying now in frustration, still sweating, and when he woke his vest and pyjamas were soaking.

The room was sunk in near darkness, the curtains drawn tightly. He tried to gauge the time by the sunlight showing under the door, but he knew it was late. The pig did not normally squeal unless it was hungry. He didn't realise at first about Gran. 'The beast's after her grub, Agnes,' he said. But of course she didn't reply.

It was unlike her not to wake first. Before my grandfather retired he used to start work at six every morning, but he never rose unless he was called. Whilst he slept on, Gran would climb from their bed and draw back the curtains. She stepped into her slippers and went down to the kitchen, already fastening her raincoat. As the kettle started to warm she would light her first cigarette and sit down by the stove. She tapped the ash into the palm of her hand, staring out through the window at the lights fading over the steelworks, the sun coming up behind them. And when her cigarette was finished and the water was ready she would tip her ash in the sink and fill a large teapot, then go out to the garden with a bucket of scraps for the pig. Much later she returned to coax Grandad awake with a cup of stewed tea.

Her routine did not alter when Grandad stopped working, nor when his leg was removed a few years after that. It was amputated just below the left knee and he was given a plastic replacement. The hospital provided a walking frame too, but his wound never properly healed and he was unable to stand for more than an hour each day. The false leg and frame soon became part of the furniture, dusted over as regularly as the sideboard and ornaments. I was born a few months after he had his operation, and in a different hospital, but Grandad always insisted I arrived on the same day in a ward next to his. He said the swap was a fair one.

Shortly after he came back to the house from the hospital Gran had their bed carried downstairs to the front room. She allowed him to sleep for an extra hour each morning but she continued to rise at just the same time. She was a small round woman and constantly busy. The pattern of her days was firmly established. It was the regularity of her daily existence which made me prefer their house to my own and when I was younger I often pleaded to be allowed to stay overnight. I slept on a lumpy mattress upstairs in the back bedroom, a part of the house they had almost abandoned. Their old bedroom remained empty, facing out to the front garden.

Grandad accepted losing his limb quite cheerfully, but neither of my grandparents would give up their cigarettes. It was the smoking, the surgeon had told them, that was responsible for his leg turning bad. Grandad would light a cigarette the moment he woke, and he lit one too as he lay listening to the pig squealing that morning. It made him cough, but it helped bring him round from his dream.

When the cigarette had burned to the stub he dropped it in a pot under his side of the bed and reached across to touch Gran. 'D'ye no hear the animal squawking, Agnes?' he said, and felt around in the space where she ought to have been. The sheets were cool and unruffled. He pushed himself upright and saw her at once. She was sitting in her nightdress by the sideboard, in the chair where she would rest each evening to remove her stockings and shoes. Her arms hung stiffly at her sides. Even in the darkness there could be no doubt what was wrong, but he continued to talk to her. 'What's up, Agnes?' he said. 'Is the motor no running this morning?'

He heaved himself from the bed slowly, feeling the damp in his clothes, the cold on his chest. His good leg creaked under his weight and he had to gasp for his breath. He paused after the effort, gripping his wheelchair, all the time watching Gran. When his breathing had steadied he lifted the brakes and rolled himself to the curtains. In the daylight he could see her more clearly. She might have been asleep the way she was seated. He approached warily, and whispered her name. 'What's up?' he asked her. Her mouth hung slightly open as if about to reply. She seemed to be returning his gaze, her eyelids partially closed, patiently watching him. He touched her chin with his thumb and shivered at the touch. 'It's nae wonder you're cold, Agnes,' he said. Her nightdress lay open, displaying her ribcage. In places the skin was as white as the cloth, but elsewhere there were blotches, like someone who had spent too long by a fire. He drew the neck of her nightdress together, fastened the buttons, then he dragged a blanket from the bed and draped her beneath it.

There was no telephone in their house because Gran wouldn't have one, she didn't like them. The clock on the sideboard showed five to eight, an hour after the milkman usually called. It was half a mile to their nearest neighbour, a mile and a half to the edge of the town. Grandad decided to wait for the paper boy. He dressed himself with fumbling hands and fished in his pocket for loose change. He would ask the boy when he came to cycle to a call box and dial 999; he would offer the coins for his trouble. Grandad always had money. Whenever I called he would give me a handful, quietly, almost secretively, whilst Gran was in the kitchen brewing tea. And later, when I got up to leave, Gran would follow me to the back door with her purse, just in case he'd forgotten. 'Did he give you your wages, son?' she would ask me. They always called it my wages and they wouldn't let me refuse.

Their bedroom downstairs had once been the front parlour, with a door that opened onto the garden, now seldom used, the lock too stiff for Grandad to open. He turned and wheeled through the smaller back room and the conservatory, into the kitchen and out to the yard, around the side of the house. The air was thick and warm and he felt the first drops of rain on his arms. At the top of the garden the pig pushed her snout over the rim of her pen and watched him approaching. She sniffed at the air and pricked up her ears, snorted and squealed excitedly. As he drew near her he offered his palm and spoke to her softly. 'Empty handed, pet,' he said. The pig butted his fingers and dropped out of sight, snuffling around the floor of her sty. Grandad stared along the rough track that led to the main road. He tapped the coins on the wheel of his chair. In the distance he could hear the first rush of traffic along the dual carriageway, an ambulance receding towards the estates of the new town.

Anna Crowe

CHAIN-STITCH

She wore this smock to sweep and dust and polish
(Chores I put off endlessly at home) –
A warm red cotton, ample and soft as she was
Under her stays and bosomy handknits; frolicsome,
Given to waltzing round the table, yet gathered,
Yoked to widowhood and childlessness.

A shake of its folds, and there's the moth-dust shining:
Tea with my great-aunt in the tiny flat;
Fresh crab, brown bread and butter, cream on fruit,
And always, the tiny window south to Cornwall –
The way the Sound would glitter, and Edgcumbe woods
Come darkly down to water; bunting and brass
On Navy Days; all this the maidenhair-fern
Embraced and veiled, where once she'd watched a ship
Stitching one line of braid away for ever.

I finger the smocking her fingers worked – chain-stitch
In coloured silks, binding us woman to woman:
I'll wear your smock, but not to dust, and break
The chains that tied you to your chores. Buttoning
Cuffs, I put on your reckless love of life,
Your passionate lust for sweet, exotic fruit –
Who still wept for *dear Phil*, but smacked your lips
At oranges, melons, apricots, peaches, grapes...

OUTSIDE THE FRAME

after *Las Meninas* by Velázquez

If I could paint, I'd have to paint you such
As Velázquez painted Philip and his queen –
A presence everything else implies; unseen
But for the mirror's distant blur and reach-
Ing-out of every pair of eyes, to touch
That place outside the frame where we imagine
Flesh-tints and splendid vestments. Roving between
The painting's world and this, their eyes beseech
Us just to stand and be there, making sense
Of fluid light or thick impasto; games
With paint; the artist at work in his own painting,
Brush poised, arrested, everything future tense,
Where canvas, mirror, sun-filled door are frames
That might embrace, like you and me, what's wanting.

WATER-MARKS

The ledger is crammed with ghosts,
transparencies, thin
as tissue, luminous as skin.
Each pressed flower persists

as nectary emptied of honey,
leaves and stalks
brush-stroked by death; silks
with colours run to rainy

weepings on the page:
tear-stains are umbels,
clusters, stars or bells
grown faint – death as seepage,

oozings that record
where wild flowers pressed
on paper, flesh on mattress,
in sap or semen, birth-waters, blood.

Pete Fortune

Suspenders

The day started with my wife and I having words. She lolls around the place on her days off dressed in jeans and sloppy old T-shirt. Fair enough. But then there she was getting dressed for work, fixing black stockings on to frilly suspenders, provocative scent in the air. 'I like to be smart for work,' she said. 'If I look good, I feel good.' I'll bet. I came out with some cheap remark and that was that – awkward silence the end result. Suspenders were never far off the agenda that day.

Later on I had to take my oldest boy to the Loreburn Hotel, to his friend's birthday party. Then I went into the bar. Des Reuter was there. I hadn't seen Des in ages. 'Hello,' he said, 'how are you doing?' He said I looked well, wondered if this was one of my usual haunts. I told him about the birthday party in the function room next door, said I was going to kill time at the bar until the party was over. His kid was at the party too, and Des had no intention of leaving either. He stretched back in his stool, yawned and scratched at his big fat belly. He said I could buy him a pint if I felt generous, then he leaned forward, resting his podgy arms on the bar.

I pulled up a stool and sat beside him. Kids were arriving all the time, an excited gaggle of ten year olds heading for the function room. I told Des it looked like it was going to be quite a party. He nodded, then yawned again, told me he was tired. 'I was at a party too,' he said, 'last night. A stag party.' He lowered his voice and told me it had been quite a night, like nothing he'd ever been to in his life before. 'Exotic dancer,' he said, exaggerating every syllable. Des glanced behind him, acknowledged one of the dads he knew. 'Good was she?' I enquired. He had his eyes closed, was grinning and making a lot of noise exhaling cigarette smoke. Des Reuter told me she wasn't so much good as positively wicked. He was forty in a little over a month's time, but he'd never seen anything like that in his life before. It was his first time. He slapped me on the back and laughed. 'Listen,' he said, 'I read the *Guardian* most days, so what do you expect?'

Brian Gibson was standing beside us, was loitering at the bar after dropping his kid off at the party. 'First time for what

Des?' he wanted to know. A couple of other dads echoed the question. Des suggested we huddle in and he would give us the gory details.

So Des Reuter told us about his school teacher cousin Gerry, who was getting married, who'd booked this dingy little room in the Thornhill Arms for his stag party. 'We'll all get pissed,' he'd told Des, 'and then maybe head off to the Indian.' But just after Des had arrived a little guy with bushy hair had demanded £5 from him, winked and mumbled something about the entertainment. 'It still didn't click,' Des told us, 'that's how bad I am.' Cousin Gerry had made a big song and dance about it all when he realised what was planned, had called them a shower of conniving bastards. Des told us this wasn't the case at all, as far as he could see it was the work of one, or at the most maybe two, of Gerry's friends. However, Gerry's face lit up when this little red-head appeared – the sort of woman you might encounter in one of those saucy *Carry On* films. She was a brassy little Cockney, but not without a certain appeal. 'If you get my meaning,' he added. She had a suitcase with her, and this mean looking guy accompanying her told them all to clear out of the room for ten minutes while she organised herself. Des Reuter told us this guy was all tattoos and biceps, assured us that no one was about to argue.

They'd left her to it and congregated back in the bar area, going on like a crowd of excited schoolboys. Des said at that stage a couple of guys had come out with some lame excuse and disappeared into the night. After a bit the mean looking character came back through and announced that she was ready for them now. The landlord warned them to behave themselves, said he would be looking in from time to time to make sure they weren't taking things too far. 'Or you'll be out on your arse,' he'd warned. So they all filed back into this dingy little room, the mean looking character reminding them to keep their hands to themselves. The woman was wearing a short nightdress affair, and clearly visible underneath was her black underwear. Suspenders and that kind of gear. There was tinny music blaring out of a tape recorder, what Des imagined was supposed to be music of an erotic nature. He said it wasn't a strip show in the sense he imagined it might be, because in no time at all she was down to her knickers. What there was of them. She'd discarded her bra, 'mock-strangled the head of History with it,' he said, then had two other guys slowly unpeel each stocking. Des was unlucky enough to be sitting right at the front and he was wearing one of those daft shirts he'd bought for his summer holidays. He felt conspicuous and just knew she would single him out at some stage. 'Sure enough,' he said, 'over she comes and tells me to take her knickers off. With my teeth.' Des Reuter told us how he'd achieved this, ignored Brian Gibson's assertion that he was sure he'd made a meal of it. Des said it wasn't easy. The only other woman he was accustomed to seeing in such a condition was his wife, but he didn't normally take her knickers off. 'Not with my teeth at any rate,' he added.

Des interrupted his story while we bought more drink in, had the man behind the bar busy himself with pints and whiskies and gin and tonics. Every so often we could hear all the kids in the function room, cheering and applauding. Next door they had a magician entertaining them. At the bar we had Des Reuter. Everyone had gathered round him by then, hanging on his every word.

He was telling us that once he'd finally removed her knickers she'd draped them over his head, then clambered up on the table and skilfully removed them between her toes. He said everyone claimed that he was blushing, and he didn't doubt for a second that he was. She'd pranced around for twenty minutes or so, climbing up on to tables and waggling her big bare bum in their faces, touching everyone up a little. A small guy with glasses who worked in insurance interrupted Des and said the whole thing sounded disgusting to him, declared it a degrading experience for all concerned. Des said he was making no moral judgement – how could he when he'd stayed till the bitter end? 'I'm telling you what happened,' he said, 'that's all.' He said this was nothing compared to what happened later on. She'd eventually announced an interval, she was going to make herself decent and go up to the bar area for a drink. 'It was weird,' Des Reuter was saying, 'seeing her put her clothes back on.' He said that had seemed more of an invasion of her privacy than anything else. He'd taken this woman's knickers off, watched her expose herself in a shameless manner, but the worst thing was being there when she stepped back into those knickers. 'We weren't watching anymore,' he said, 'we were seeing.' This was for real, not part of an act.

So they'd all gathered back in the bar area, pouring more

beer down their throats and yapping about the red-head. A few of them had admitted feeling anxious about the whole thing, were worried about who might walk in the door. Des told us to remember that these were essentially professional people, men who felt they'd reputations to keep intact. As well as teachers, there was a fair sprinkling of solicitors, accountants, that kind of line. Even a social worker. Des grinned and said *he* probably read the *Guardian* too. 'Not your archetypal slap and tickle brigade,' he said. He went on to tell us about a Labour councillor being there, 'politically correct,' Des said, 'and yet there he was at the front bawling louder than almost anyone.' He wasn't about to name him though. 'With a name like mine,' he said, 'it wouldn't do to get involved in slanderous gossip.' The little insurance man had a fair idea who Des was talking about, said the same guy would probably claim attendance allowance.

More booze was being ordered, and Des was telling us that maybe the biggest surprise was the presence of a man he used to work beside. A man whose wife had recently committed suicide. Him there and his wife not long dead. Des said a couple of years back she'd lost two good friends in quick succession, these two youngish women who'd both died of cancer. It had a traumatic effect on her. She'd gone a bit odd and started drinking a lot. Empty vodka bottles were turning up all over the place, but when challenged she would just clam up. Refuse to talk about it. Then she'd become severely anxious, and eventually hypochondriac and unable to leave the house. Des could recall the poor guy telling him at the time that she had become immersed in the grim certainty that she would succumb to some terrible disease. Would die of cancer just like her friends. He'd told Des he was at his wit's end, said she was a mystery to him, truth be told all women were a mystery to him. Always had been. And now here he was, ogling the red-head, maybe thinking that staring at female flesh would help him unravel some of the mystery. Des said certainly there wasn't much being left to the imagination.

Brian Gibson said didn't it seem an incredible thing for a hypochondriac to do, to go and top herself? 'Talk about confronting your worst fears,' one of the dads added. The little insurance man with the glasses said suicide usually invalidated life policies. He had mixed views on this being the case, went on to talk at some length about his work. He was a strange, intense little man, seemed keen that we acknowledge his academic credentials. He had a degree, wasn't one of those people who'd packed up some crummy shift work job to peddle insurance round the doors. Someone else had read somewhere that the best way to judge a man was to see what kind of shape his woman was in. 'How must that guy feel,' he said, 'in those circumstances?' Brian Gibson told him to belt up, he was huffing and puffing at Des to get on with the story. 'Tell us about the red-head Des,' he was saying, 'what did she get up to next?'

Des told us that after their break they'd all huddled together in that dusty little room, each hoping she wouldn't single them out. There wasn't even the pretence of a strip show this time because she hadn't a stitch on from the very beginning. Everyone had swallowed a fair bit of beer by then, so there was a desperate procession to the gents' toilet and back. Whenever the door of that room opened they all diverted their attention from the red-head, anxious to know who it was. Were afraid of their filthy secret being revealed. It could have been the landlord, 'grumpy old Hugh,' he said, 'about to stop the show, or worse.' Some of the older kids from the Academy were known to involve themselves in under-age drinking sessions there. 'Imagine some of *them* wandering in,' he said, 'with half the bloody staff drooling at some naked woman.' He said it wouldn't do much for their credibility, not exactly enhance career prospects. 'So every time that door opened,' he said, 'we all turned round.' Brian Gibson offered to buy Des a drink. 'I'll buy you all a drink,' he said, 'if Des promises to stop waffling and tell us what she did next.'

What she did next was plank herself on cousin Gerry's knee, take off his tie and loop it around his neck. 'Then she led him on to the floor,' Des told us, 'on to what space there was in front of the tables.' She'd taken his glasses off and done the strangest of things with them. 'I mean, they disappeared,' he said, 'totally.' Brian Gibson took some convincing. 'Really,' Des said, 'but that was nothing to what happened later on.' So she'd led Gerry on to the floor, and pretty soon had him stripped right down to his Y-fronts. 'We were pretty sure she would stop at that,' Des told us, 'but we couldn't be certain.' He said at least *he* couldn't be certain, because where was his yardstick? Brian Gibson made some bawdy comment about yardstick, then Des went on to tell us about the baby oil appearing. 'She rubbed him all over with the stuff,' he said, 'even reaching down into his Y-fronts.' Then they could hardly believe their eyes when she peeled them right off. There he was, cousin Gerry, lying bollock naked on the floor of the Thornhill Arms. 'A most peculiar thing to see,' Des told us, and no one was doubting it. Poor Gerry looked petrified, must have been wondering what was about to happen next.

Then the man behind the bar wandered over, interrupted Des's story. He wanted to know if there was a Brian Gibson in the bar, said there was a phone call for him. 'Wait till I'm back,' he pleaded. Through in the function room we could hear a succession of 'oohs' and 'aahs', followed by lots of laughter. Des was wanting to order more drink, but the man behind the bar was staring up at the television set, was flicking from channel to channel with the remote control device. We caught a fleeting glimpse of an old black and white film, then an acrobat leaping from bar to bar. Next there was a rugby match, then we were treated to a subliminal image of some luscious beauty fellating a chocolate bar. Finally he gave up and switched the set off. Through in the function room there were calls of *Hip Hip Hooray.*

One of the dads, a little man everyone referred to as Tub, said it sounded as if the kids were having a good time. He said it sounded as if cousin Gerry had had a good time too, a lot different from what he could recall of *his* stag night. They'd played darts and dominoes then, maybe traded a dirty story or two. He said he thought he preferred it that way.

Des said not to get him wrong, he could see in retrospect what a squalid business it had been. Not something he was particularly proud of. They were supposed to be enlightened men, 'ostensibly a gathering of late twentieth century modern males,' he said, yet there they all were hollering at some poor woman waggling her bare bum about. He had a sick kind of grin on his face, admitted that alcohol was largely to blame for their behaviour. 'Things you do when you're drunk,' he said. One of the dads said alcohol was a negative drug, told us this while he ordered another large gin and tonic. 'Huxley,' he was saying, 'I think it was Aldous Huxley who described alcohol as one of the crudest drugs known to man.' He went on to tell us that Aldous Huxley chose to depart this life spaced out on mescaline. 'Maybe he was right about alcohol,' he told us, 'I mean it could be that if we looked around with an open mind we'd find a more acceptable social drug than alcohol.' One of the other dads whose face I recognised from somewhere said he used tranquillisers from time to time. 'Little blue pills,' he said. 'The doc gives me them at holiday times, for the flight.' Des asked him what it was about flying that scared him so. 'I'm not afraid of flying,' he replied, 'but the doc thinks I am. He's under the impression that I do a lot of it too.' He said those little blue pills gave him some pleasant days at work, when he felt the need of it. 'I'm not endorsing it, or even trying to justify it,' he said, 'but it suits me. It's kind of like having a holiday without taking time off.' The dad who'd started all this talk about drugs was getting on about Huxley again, talking about *Brave New World* and soma, but Brian Gibson interrupted him. He was back from the phone and snarling at Des to get on with his story. 'Come on Des, what happened next?'

'Where was I?' Des wanted to know. Tub obliged, reminded him that cousin Gerry was bollock naked on the floor, being covered all over in baby oil. Des informed us that at that stage someone had put a chair in front of the door and sat on it. 'I mean we would probably all have ended up arrested,' he said, 'and then divorced.' He went on to tell us how the red-head had sat on Gerry's chest and invited suggestions as to what to do next. They were baying like a pack of wild animals by then, making all sorts of obscene suggestions. Then she'd sig-nalled to the mean looking character who promptly went over and switched the music off. She said normally the show would be over at that stage, but because they'd all been such good sports she was willing to carry on. 'She said she'd finish with something *really* special,' Des said, 'if we'd produce another £3 per head.' Gerry was protesting like mad, but he couldn't move, what with her sitting on top of him, and besides every-one was ignoring him anyway. Des said it was as if they had been seized by a collective madness. 'Mob hysteria,' the insur-ance man suggested. 'Poor Gerry,' Des was saying, 'lying there like that. You wouldn't believe what she did to him next, in front of us all too.'

One of the dads interrupted, said he wondered what drove women like that to act in such a way. 'I mean is it poverty, or what?' he wanted to know. Little Tub said a lot of these dancers, if you could call them that, were prostitutes, were women who'd been driven off the streets through fear of

AIDS. They could probably earn as much, if not more, this way, and be a whole lot safer into the bargain. The little insurance man joined in, wanted to tell us about a documentary he'd caught just the other night. He said it had made grim viewing, featured a couple who'd both developed AIDS as a result of the husband having a crazy one night stand. 'There's three kids there,' he said, 'and pretty soon they're going to be orphans. Can you even start to imagine?' One of the dads reckoned it must be an insurance man's nightmare, 'two bad lives in the one household.' The insurance guy ignored this remark – we all ignored this remark – but Des told me on the quiet later that it just showed you, nowadays nothing was sacred in the search for a belly laugh.

The little insurance man was going on about promiscuity in general, was telling us about someone who used to work in his office. 'This guy,' he was saying, 'married with kids, but he would have it away almost every chance he got.' Someone had challenged him one day, asked what he would do if he discovered that his wife had been playing around. He said he would divorce her. He said all *his* encounters were purely physical, in essence meant nothing to him. He knew his wife well enough, and if she slept with someone else it would suggest an emotional commitment. He said his wife wouldn't sleep with another man unless she was in love with him. Which was why he would terminate the marriage pronto. He wasn't necessarily suggesting this was the case with all women, but it certainly was with his wife. He said men could hop in and out of bed without becoming caught up in any romantic nonsense.

Des Reuter had finished yet another pint, was laughing and singing *Ain't necessarily so*. He said a guy he knew had been seeing another woman one time, just having fun and messing around together. 'I mean this wasn't even a sexual relationship, at least that's what he claimed.' They just enjoyed each other's company, revelled in the illicit nature of the whole episode. Then one day Des had met up with him in the pub and he was pissed as a fart. He'd gone crashing off his bar stool in the end, so Des had bundled him into his car and driven him home. He admitted to Des that he was in an emotional mess, didn't know which way to turn. He'd ended up falling in love with this woman, and him married with three kids. The woman had become aware of how he felt and she'd told him in effect to clear off. The poor bugger had bumped into her that very afternoon and it had set him off again. She'd just walked right on by, and he told Des she was smiling at him, or maybe laughing. He said that had been his big mistake, never learning how to tell the difference. He could never tell whether she was smiling at him, or laughing at him. Des said any time he saw this guy now he seemed fine, 'but how can you tell what's going on deep down?' He was shaking his head and telling us that situations like that were poison, was of the opinion that life was a lot simpler spent pottering about in the greenhouse, slippers toasting by the fire.

Little Tub reckoned that what it all boiled down to was your kids. 'Couple we know,' he said, 'their marriage broke up and now they're in the middle of a divorce.' He said it sounded hard going, had turned pretty ugly, but at least there were no kids involved. 'They're big enough to take the knocks,' he said, 'but if kids are involved, well, that's another matter altogether.' All of the dads were nodding their heads, agreeing that the kids had to be the primary concern. 'Of course you're sometimes tempted,' one was saying, 'but you have to think of the consequences. The effect it might end up having on your marriage. On your kids. You can't get away with much in a small town like this you know.' Someone else was saying that kids kept you on the straight and narrow, stopped you straying too far. *Just not worth it* was the general consensus. Des Reuter was about drunk by then, was asking why a marriage always broke *up* and never *down*. 'Surely it should be *down*?' he was saying. The insurance guy said that when a couple split it was always the mother who ended up with custody. 'I couldn't start to imagine living a life where my kids played a peripheral role,' he said.

A waitress appeared with great stacks of glasses, told the man behind the bar there was plenty more to come. 'It's hell in there,' she told him, indicating the function room. There were little beads of sweat on her forehead, causing her hair to become plastered down. Des Reuter was studying her rump and pulling a funny face. Little Tub was going on about his wife, said she sometimes complained he put more emphasis on being a good dad than he did on being a good husband. He was aware of it being meant as an insult, that it was delivered as an accusation, but none the less it had secretly pleased him. 'She'd at least implied that I'm a good dad,' he said, 'and that's important. You're not a dad for very long, not in that sense

anyway.' He reminded us that our kids would be grown up
and out of it before we knew where we were. Des was nodding, he could find an affinity in that. He said he felt he had a
deeper bond with his kids than he had with his wife. 'It's not a
conditional love with your kids,' he said, 'not dependent on
behaviour. It is with man and wife. Divorce proves that.' He
said your kids could tear your balls out in your sleep, but
you'd still love them. 'Deep down you would,' he said. Brian
Gibson assured us that he loved his kids too, even if sometimes he felt he didn't like them. 'But just finish your story
Des,' he was saying, 'what did she do to Gerry?' He'd caught
the mood of the moment. 'Come on,' everyone was saying,
'get on with it.'

So Des took us back to cousin Gerry lying helpless on the
floor of the Thornhill Arms, reminded us in a theatrical manner about the baby oil and the *special* the £3 had bought. 'She
came out with this aerosol spray,' he said, 'and sprayed this
cream on him.' First his nose got it, then she licked it all off.
'Where next boys,' she'd wanted to know, but had ignored the
reply and sprayed each nipple instead. 'She licked that off too,'
Des said, 'really taking her time about it.' Then a condom
appeared, and when it was out of the foil she'd made a big
show of stretching it out as far as it would go. 'Christ
almighty,' he said, 'if the door had opened then... can you
imagine the reaction of grumpy old Hugh?' He said she was
kneeling over Gerry, strategically placed, and with them all
roaring her on. Then she'd taken the condom and...

... and from behind the closed doors of the function room
there was a lot of cheering going on, followed by laughter. We
could hear the pounding of feet, like a storm approaching,
than all hell was let loose. Someone shouted *DAD* and we all
turned round.

Joy Fraser

A POEM ABOUT DRUMS

Thump   thump   thump

Thump   thump   thump thump   thump
This is a poem about drums

Thump   thump thump thump

Thump   thump thump   thump
Thump

THUMP
If said correctly, once in a million years this poem

has a meaning...   ..ful rhythm (to make up
                                      for the words   )

All the rest of the time it

is just a drum
thumping

at the back. All

forlorn > Sniff
(But quite jolly, really)

Can you hear

it?
Thump   thump

crescendo   loud thump
Do NOT LaUGH AT tHis poEm :
You are maybe not jollificated enough to love it.

That   's not my problem
Thump thump
diminuendo   soft thump

presto   fast thump
apassionato   ...dud thump

Thump   thump   thump
Thump thump   t   h   u   m   p

This is a poem about drums

The enD

Raymond Friel

ABROAD

for Martin & Maggie

Guzzling Caesars
in the hissing swelter of the gas fire,
we dutifully sat
through the snaps of Canada,
the black stray *Lucky*
coiled on the cushion between us.

Unimpressive unlinked
to memory, the thrill or gag
of seeing *me*... a white-legged blur
woodenly offers a hillside packed with trees;
a maybe-a-smudge a mile to port
the showering lash of a humpback's tail;
a mofette of whale breath
a running jump away, pure evil.
& then the damn thing broke!

The lasagne browned
& the Valpolicella breathed
at an unpeopled table
as mein host, my oldest friend,
thumped around & slammed back
in with *Nagano 1990*...
On the brink in the karaoke bar,
the foamhead microphone limp by his side,
pursed mouth shining,
eyes of the Antichrist at Armageddon's rally...
'The split second
before I fell into the PA'
& perhaps the morning after,
a snow-capped Hokusai,
the sky a Marian blue...
I have sat here facing the Cold Mountain
for twenty-nine years,
sort of thing.

I tore into
the garlic bread, jabbering
abroad... your eyebrow raised
to guillotine my piddly plans;
while after the fruit bowl, the Blue Label
& three hours sleep, at the end
of our long & verdant slide home,
if home is where the rent is, London
jammed in a mucilage of lights,
dimming towards the millennium.

Graham Fulton

EASTERN BLOC ICONS EMBRACE THE WEST

Lenin pulls roubles
                    from the dispenser,
sprints to the
                    nearest dance.
He has
        his latest statement
in his hand,
                    embalming fluid
in his veins.
                    He has

a way
        with the girls,
a beard
            that tickles
when they snog.
                    He lies back,
thinks of the Tsar
                    when they point
their lips
            at his head.

Yeltsin winks
                    and sings peasant songs,
weighs mince
                    in a butcher's shop.
He charms
            the ladies with patter
and tripe.
            'Oh Boris,
you are a tease'
                    they say.
He looks

good in
a blood-streaked coat,
                    flaunts his
nifty cleaver technique.
                        A cow
in the shape
            of a Baltic state
falls from its hook
                when he opens the till.

Stalin is dressed
                as Santa Claus
in the basement
                of a department store.
His warcoat is buttoned
                        to the throat
beneath his
        scarlet festive top.
He smiles

        his best inscrutable smile,
goes hoho on
                occasions.
He is
        vastly unpopular
with the kiddies
                who see his woolly beard
is false,
        blitz him with books
when he goes
            for his tea.

Mayakovsky flogs
                subversive tracts
and recipes from
                a pavement hut.
He has
        a cigarette
in his head,
            a cloth cap
in his mouth.
                He wears

snug britches,
                   thrusts his groin,
whispers useless
                   fashion ideas
in Women's ears,
                   blows
out his brains
                   when
they least expect
it.

Robin Fulton

INSIDE THE SPACIOUS TOMB

The white glow from the wakened corpse
brightens the faces of the two
staring angels, one left one right,
and the back of the third, who lifts
lightly the jagged square stone slab
from the tomb's round-arched opening

The square never fitted the arch
The reclining head is too small
and the legs too long   The whiteness
sees with the eye of lightning things
that don't fit   It is eager   Soon
it will ambush the blind dawn trees

but already it has cut short
eighteen centuries and startled
Mr Blake, in South Molton Street

William Gilfedder

I hate when people rabbit on
About the simple joys of nature
There's nothing simple in it
Sure it's nice to go for long walks in the country
It's all very relaxing
But it's nothing to do with nature
Nature has reached its present state of development
Through thousands of years of evolution
Based on the basic law of tooth and claw
Which to this are held as if by centrifugal force
Some of the most complex intricate and incomprehensible
Abstractions known to science
So when someone says to me O for the joys of the country
I feel like going out and stripping the bark
From every tree in sight.

Valerie Gillies

THE SAPLING GREYHOUND

I like to meet my friend the greyhound:
For her, I hang my head upside down
And she takes my ear in her white teeth.
I feel the bite of winter nip the heath.

SLATERS

The scaffolding is up.
Two slaters sit on a block
facing each other.
They flake and knock
shapes from the grey stack,
raise their hands to chop
at the split-thin plates
with clippers.
Their collars hang loose
at the backs of their necks
like manes.
They are winged
with flying slivers
like feathers.
Ready to slate,
they are two confronted,
two griffins at the gate.

John Glenday

PALE FLOWER

*In 1774 the first anatomical dissection of a
human body ever carried out in Japan was
performed using Dutch textbooks upon the
body of the famous Geisha, Pale Flower.*

A longitudinal incision
through the skull reveals
a brain soft but resilient;

the tongue well anchored in its –
page forty three – cartilaginous bed.
Trachea clear of speech.

That fist-sized mash of sour grains
in the gut would be her last meal, stained
with altered blood.

Good musculature abdominally,
though paler than the illustration.
Pale Flower. Bloodlessly beautiful.

Let us fold back these petals: note
how the pistil remains
lush, even beyond death.

Such is the vessel she was.
See here, where that slack root,
her obedience,

adheres; the gourd hangs
moist but sterile.
That's enough. Returning to the head,

these arteries which channel
through the neck sustained her intellect.
More necessary still, this fine mesh

here and here, spread strands of blood,
like saffron, through her cheeks,
whenever it was right, or so desired.

FIRSTBORN

for Daniel

I watch him brace both fists across his chest,
clutching a hidden rope which strains
down through the sheets, into his sleep.

Something has tied him to a something he can't be rid of,
or else there's some useless thing out there,
some slick, unwieldy dead-weight he just won't give up.

A burden heavier than his five years, settling
into the darkness, snagged on pondweed and roots.
He'll never get it to move.

When I stroke his head to settle him, his hands spring open
like a trap and he cries out a shrill, frail,
desperate, battered-brain-stem cry

as that little figment of his life, or mine, goes tumbling
headlong through his dream and just for the time
it takes to drown, comes true.

Jane Harris

BITS AND PIECES AT JUMBO

Finished. No more Yvonne. It's easy. She doesn't want me enough. So I go, I'm out. I'm gone and I don't come back. Really. These north European women are all same. And the Americans. You see the way she is, she fix them with her eyes, she don't see me any more. I need a woman who is respecting me. When I am at work or with my friends having drinks, I must know, she is home, not at the supermarket, sucking the men into her eyes while she push the trolley. Giving her smile to them. It's a pity. Believe me. We could have had the nice life together, really or even short. Relationship, but good. Poor, but nice life. But I'm already out.

Actually by the time I get off the train Nelson has vamoosed into the crowds again. Now I'm beginning to work out why this happens okay. First I thought it was because he wanted to be on his own. Own space that sort of thing but it's nothing like that at all. Shall I tell you what it is. It's because he's jealous you see. Insanely jealous god even more jealous than me if that's possible. Look a couple of weeks ago he left a restaurant, waltzed out didn't even touch his gambas and you know why because he thought I was flirting with the waiters. Ridiculous isn't it. Jealousy leaps in and old Nelson scuttles off, grinding his dentures. Just now on the train he probably imagined I was eyeing up that young soldier's crotch or something. This Latin, this Latin inverted commas temperament is so different from what one is used to in England. I mean sex in bloody Berkshire was a bit of grim thrusting after closing time at The Horns or wherever yeh. Here in Lisbon it's Nelson, his mouth glistening after a good dinner, sliding both hands up my skirt and getting his fingers inside my, my knickers. Etcetera. He says, 'Yvonne, let me love you,' he says and his eyes are sort of damp. To think I had to wait till 40 odds to discover. Well. What it can be like. You know. Anyway there's no sign of him so I pootle along the seafront to Monte. And back again, to Estoril. Nada. So he must have gone back to the grandmother's that's where he lives you see, with his grandmother. Not unusual in Portugal for a man in his 30s to be living with his family it's the poverty actually. In Angola Nelson had a black momma to dress him, private tuition the whole shooting match. Chicken farm or something. Then of course they had to come back, lost everything, live now in what's virtually actually it's practically a shack. Grandmother rents the whole place for the same price per month as I pay for my bikini line. Honestly. Some medieval law or something. Anyway odds on he's sloped off there, so I park my bum at a cafe. No point in rushing things. Tactics that's what this situation calls for.

Maybe three days I get her out of my system. Today is Saturday. I have another woman Tuesday. Believe me. I fix one and I have one. She can be ugly or she can be stupid. I make her beautiful, intelligent. Maybe I have more than one. I am like the Arab you see, the Arab is in me. Yvonne is not ugly, she is attractive woman in 30s. But. This doesn't matter. She can be looking good but she don't find me.

I have this absolutely brilliant bloody brainwave on my second spritzer. Flowers. I'll send him flowers yeh. Appeal to his ego you see. Very much the Leo is Nelson. Dark curly hair. Teeth like tombstones. 'I have to take care of the teeth, Yvonne,' he says. 'The teeth are important.' They're not his own though. Not the front ones anyway mind you you'd never guess. Bit of a Romeo in his time Nelson. Maybe even I suspect a gigolo actually. Not now of course not now. Anyway he's developed, watchamacallit not eczema the other thing, psoriasis. Not his face just his body. When it's bad he looks like, damn what's that actor. Rod Schneider that's him, Illustrated Man, did you see it? It doesn't bother me. Not much. Except when he wanders round the flat with no clothes on, scratching. Then I'm sweeping bit of him up for yonks after. Clogs the shower yeh. The plughole.

Apart to cinema, there are three things important in life Yvonne. Let me tell you. The one is having the good sunglasses, like these. Really. It's the true. Second is easy, that's good shirts, maybe three only, but good. And the last it's the expensive perfume. Like this. You can smell. Smell. I get this one from a woman I fuckid. It was last year don't worry. Trust me. The sunglasses, the shirts, the perfume. These are what is important for man. And. To be really a man, really, he must have the 10 per cent that is the feminine, like Malkovitch in *Dangerous Liaisons*. So. For 90 per cent of him is male. And then for the rest, he has the female quality. This is what make him really the special. Really.

Lucky old me, there's a florist's in the terrace near the casino and I point out the stems I want. Oh I know I've lived here a year but I don't know the names of bloody flowers in Portuguese do I. I choose red and white ones only. Someone sent me a bouquet once made entirely, entirely of red and white flowers. Stunning. Not quite stunning enough to save that particular romance actually but I did like the effect. You know what red and white mean of course. Passion okay and purity. Quite good. Quite good for our relationship. A sort of, metaphor. Mmm. So this woman in the shop speaks to me in English, says it'll be an hour before the bouquet is ready doesn't this country drive you absolutely screaming mad? The poor Germans die of frustration every summer just waiting for a beer. I'm sure yeh, I'm sure if I was dark instead of blonde I'd get quicker service. Praps I ought to stop using bleach. Nelson likes it though, he says blonde is exotical. Isn't that sweet. Exotical. He has such endearing mispronunciations. My favourite okay is the one he does on 'eedee' words. Like instead of saying kissed, he says kissid. Kissid. Smokid. Killid. I've explained the difference to him but he's so stubborn.

Let me love you hmm? Let me love you. We can make love, not sex not easy fucking. Hmm? I wanna fuck you, do you wanna be fuckid?

I could go back to the apartment and wait till the flowers are ready but I don't know. Walking from one room to another. I never feel much like sitting down in any of them actually. I do go out a lot mind you. Spend a lot of time in the supermarket. I like that. Getting my bits and pieces. That's where Nelson and I met actually. What else do I do, Royal Navy docks sometimes and the lads invite us English girls aboard for drinks. Etcetera. That's usually good. Mostly I lie on the beach when I'm off work. Go to cafes. Only drink spritzers okay. Meet men like Nelson. Ah no look now there's only one of him. Only one Nelson.

What is this? What is this Yvonne? You don't know. Well,
I will tell you. It is a flea. It is a flea that was in your bed. Who
has been here? Who has been in your bed, hmm? Oh sure, a
cat. A cat. A cat a cat a cat a cat. You expect me to believe
this? Your lies, you deception. Don't lie me Yvonne. Tell me
only the true. Trust me. Follow me. Hmm?

Nelson says I ought to put an advert in the Anglo
Portuguese News for another girl to share. Well I was going to
in May but that's when we met and I sort of hoped... Nelson
doesn't stay that often as it turns out. Has to look after the
grandmother you see. She's on crutches you know, very reli-
gious. Calls me madame. Sits at the window all day dressed in
black like they do, clutching her tranny and babbling mass or
something. When she's got a headache, she wears this scarf
round her head like a bandana, with potato slices wedged
behind it. I took some almond biscuits round once and she got
all embarrassed about the potatoes, tried to cover them up
with her hands. 'Batatas batatas' she kept saying and showed
me her gums. Sucked the almond biscuits to a pulp and spat
the nuts out. Charming. No teeth you see. 80 odds. So Nelson
takes care of her. And he works, so many hours, unsociable
hours. Normal for a security guard.

I tell her, one day we will have the nice cloths over everything, on the table, the bed. A small house, maybe in Sintra.
And the rugs everywhere. Nice fruits in the kitchen, some
cakes and the good wine. Always the good wine. But for this, I
must have a better job.

Just arriving with flowers. Hardly original is it? It ought to
be something fabulous. Cinematic. Nelson adores cinema.
When we've had a few he always says he wants to make a
movie actually. Or start some business. All pretty dodgy if you
ask me. Sometimes I wonder, I wonder if he's only interested in
me for capital. Not that I've enough to lend him christ I'm a
secretary. Well I work for an English company so I earn a bit
more than average, bank manager's happy yes. And if I did go
back to Henley, well I'd make a packet in boats. Well I'd go
back only dad keeps nagging at me. But Nelson you see auto-
matically assumes just like the rest of them okay, that the
British people are rolling in it.

The computer it's a wonderful thing you know Yvonne. Really. Maybe one day I can be home with you, or some honest woman. And playing with my son. Be running five nightclubs. In Europe. I just tap the computer. Easy. But I need someone to say: Here you are Nelson, you're good, take this money, have your business. It happens Yvonne. And then I find what I want, and I give up the drinking and the cigarettes. Believe me. I'm a sport boy, really. Maybe one day I go to Algarve to make a movie. I can take one woman. We have laughs, drinks. Then I take another one to Paris. Easy. Or. I have just one honest woman, home.

What about some small boys to deliver the flowers. A procession. Nelson would love that, and I can be head of casting okay. Spoilt for choice really down at the beach so I stick the old shades on and pick the first group of lads on the steps. 'Boa Tarde,' I say, 'queria quatros o cinqos meninos.' Well, they're astonished you know, who's this attractive foreign woman asking for four or five boys. So I explain about the flowers. 'Comprendo. So para as flors.' Sounds good. SOUnds good. But. It's not going as smoothly as I expected actually. Accent's alright, it's vocabulary that's lacking. Nelson said I'd learn good Portuguese with him but all he's taught me in four months is 'my man' and 'squeeze me tight'. Wish I knew the word for deliver. I flourish a one hundred escudo note. Bingo. There's a skirmish and I gain surplus boys and even some grown men okay. 'Nao, nao,' I have to say to one old guffer with liver spots, 'velho, velho. So os pequenos meninos.' I show a height with my hand to demonstrate that anyone over twelve can forget it. Thank heavens, one of the lads grabs four of his friends and throws them down on the sand at my feet. Then he silences the crowd and turns to me. 'My name is Nuno,' he says, 'What we do for this escudos?' 'Thank god, you speak English,' I say. You know. It's always such a relief when they can make themselves understood. So I explain what I want them to do okay, slowly of course, miming all the actions, and then he interprets. When he finishes, there is unanimous jeering. Nuno grins at me over his bare shoulder. He's got bleached fluff all over his skin, just like a little animal and he says: 'Then we go in your hotel, yes?' 'Hotel?' I say, 'I don't live in a hotel, I have apartment.' Someone in the crowd crows out like a rooster, appartament, appartament! We all laugh and sweat dribbles down my leg. 'No Nuno,' I say, 'We just deliver flowers to my friend's house, we don't go to my apartment.' And I smile reassuringly at any adults nearby. Well, you can't be too careful can you?

One mistake, I make the one mistake. And. You know what it is? I care for her. I get her under the skin. Here. She is here. All the time. But, how can it be? I take her to see my friends at Sintra. Just to say, look, this is the one, this time, this woman will be the one. And maybe later in the cafe my friends laugh at me, hmm, for some stupid things, they are laughing and laughing. And in this moment when she should be standing by me and showing the friends that she cares about me. What happen? She is laughing, laughing. And everybody is laughing more. It's the big joke. So, how can it be?

So there I am, outside Nelson's house, my arms full of flowers, surrounded by barefoot schoolboys all hopping about in dayglo shorts and nudging each other. I find myself thinking thank god I'm a stranger yeh. The boys tiptoe across the yard, all waxy skin and dark curls like mahogany angels. Nuno knocks and I crouch down behind the wall. The two smallest hold up the bouquet. After about an aeon the latch rattles and I don't believe it, the Grandmother drags herself onto the landing with her crutches. Damn damn. She never usually opens the door. She's wearing her scarf, means she's got a headache. 'Batatas batatas,' she says and shows you her gums. She's doing it again now to the boys yeh. Probably frighten the life out of them. It's too depressing to watch.

Watching the guys in the cafe, at the beach, on the train. Giving them your smile. These guys are good, hmm? They're smart, you smile at them and then, they have you. Like that. Plaff. Especially you Yvonne, because you are easy to have, easy. You are easy having, easy fuckid. North European women. You are always same, always be the same. I give you chances chances. Because I give all, you know, all. Everything to women. I test them, they fuck me with their deception and I go. I'm out. Really, really. I can never trust you. So now I find the honest woman.

I walk to the corner and count out the cash. After a minute the lads scoot round, panting. 'Okay?' 'Yes,' says Nuno. 'The man not in home but we give to the lady. She had got a headache.' Oh well. He probably did his best. I press the notes into his hand and flash him a smile, the one that crinkles my nose yeh.

But what you think, maybe first we have more one dinner together, hmm, last chance hmm? What you think, Yvonne. We have wine, spend the last night together. Because tomorrow you don't have me I'm working and after, I am with someone else. Come have a dinner. Hmm? Then if you want me for some days, another time, just call me. We can have a nice time, make love you know how I like to make love, not sex, not easy fucking. We can do this. Trust me, follow me. Come on. I wanna fuck you do you wanna be fuckid? Hmm? Tell me Yvonne, do you wanna be fuckid?

Thinks, thinks. If Nelson's not home, he's probably gone drinking in Cascais. I could hop on the train, be there in no time. Pick up some bits and pieces at Jumbo. Have a wander. Bump into Nelson inverted commas, accidentally. We can have drinks, dinner. Etcetera. There's that fish place where the staff are so friendly. Pricey but you don't mind paying over the odds for something decent do you. They do a nice Calimari actually, wonderful Vinho Verde.

W.N. Herbert

THE SELKIES

I

It was his turn to abuse the woman. All the others had done it and now there was no getting out of it. He knew he didn't have to do anything much, but that wasn't the point. He could, for instance, simply walk into the room drunk and say aggressively: 'Where's ma tea? Why's ma tea no oan the table, you stupit wumman?' That would do it.

Of course the others did not suffer qualms like him. Some of them had hit her, spat in her face, cursed her mother and the fruit of her womb. He thought about that phrase as he waited his turn: fruit of her womb. He imagined the woman walking around with an apple inside her belly. It would have to be an apple, though he sort of saw a pear: two pears in fact, on a plate. The plate was made of dark, pewtery substance and dug into her spine.

He imagined the woman sitting in a room similar to this one: brown walls with a gas mantle, no furniture. If he rolled up her blouse at the front, would he be able to feel the hard rim of the plate through her belly? Naturally it was thoughts like this which impeded him, which got between him and the task in hand. He remembered the beating he had got over the Budgerigar Incident, as he had called it.

The Instructor – a man in his fifties, with grey hair rutted from the comb, yellowing with Brylcreme – had shouted at him again and again from a few inches. He remembered noting that his teeth were yellow as well, thinking that the phlegm in his throat would be yellow from the cigarettes.

'How can ye no get it right? It's a simple wee word: hen. Onybody can remember that! H-E-N, hen.'

Was this the smell of yellow? he had wondered, inhaling the Instructor's warm breath.

'It's because of the bird-watching book. It keeps putting names intae ma heid. I cannae concentrate.'

'But you do not call a wumman a parakeet. Do you call a wumman a parakeet, Tosh?'

This was to one of the Instructor's star pupils, a tall lad

with a hook nose and black hair. The skin on the nose was stretched tight, and the boy kept smirking. It was as though he didn't have enough skin to cope with the size of his nose, and the smirk was the result.

'No Mister Salter, but I'm no a smart wee dickheid.'

'Say it Sammie. Fur the love o God say it.'

'Hullawrerr...b...budgerigar.'

Once it had been established that the Instructor had meant to nut him, everyone piled in. Tosh had been delighted to, given Sammie's propensity for ridiculing him in the bar. At the time, he had been a little surprised that some of them, the ones he had thought of as friendly towards him, had not held back their boots. None of that surprised him now: he had worked out what they were being taught.

He had also worked out the Instructor didn't understand the implications of his own lessons. Sammie had grasped this the week after the Budgerigar Incident. Davie, one of those he had thought of as 'friendly', had asked the question.

'Whit maks them dae it, sir?'

'Dae whut, Davie?'

'Lie and deceive us, sir, and give oor positions away to the Amazons. I mean the Amazons kill them as collaborators onyway, so why dae they dae it?'

'Aye, that's a good question, Davie. Well the answer is they canna help it. It's in their nature. That's why ye've got to stamp on their nature as hard as ye can. Put it this way, dae ony of you know the story of the selkie bride?'

Everybody said no, though they all did. Everybody liked stories, which, with the exception of war stories about the Commandos and the Amazons, were strictly controlled. The Instructor was perhaps a little soft on them in this respect, or so Sammie had overheard the Director saying. But, as the man had replied in his own defence, 'they're jist laddies.'

'Well there was this fisherman warked his own wee boat and wisna beholden tae onywan, and he was far from aa the fighting and didna care to capture his ain wife. So he decided tae net a selkie instead, and huv her for his bride. Now the selkies all came out in the evenin and sunned themsels on a sandbank in the bay, sae he laid a net across the bay whaur the bank wad be, and waited.

'That evenin was lovely, and twa selkies came up oot o the sea tae sing and watch the sunset. But when they rolled onto the bank where the net was streitched, he didna dae a thing, he jist lay quiet in his boat and waited. He was waiting to see whit sex the selkies were and as soon as they started singing he knew he'd got himself a wife, so he hauled on the net and snared them up and soon he had two selkies in his boat, one man and one woman. They were stark naked except for a wee sark of fur that he kent was their seals' skins.

'So he cut the throat of the man and snatched up the shirt of the wumman, and rowed for home. And the wumman was weeping and wailing but she couldna get away fur the shirt of fur that he was holdin. And the male selkie's body turned back intae a seal, and he cut off the blubber and dried the meat, and he shut the female in his hut. And they lived thegither the haill o that winter and he got her wi child.'

Everybody in the class sniggered at this point, because the Instructor was fairly into his story, or he would never have used such a quaint expression for fucking.

'But when the bairn was born the fisherman had to go out again for more food and he left the wumman locked up with her child. But he didna take the wumman's shirt wi him, so when he came back he foond his baby lyin in the hut by its lane wi a knife laid across its throat.'

'Did she cut the baby's craw, sir?' This was Tosh, alert for a potential gory variation on the perennial theme.

'No, but she micht as well've done, for aa that puir man could do for it. She'd jist upped and left him wi it, and gone back to the sea. And what is the moral of my tale, Davie?'

'That ye cannae trust a wumman, sir.'

'Not just that, laddie. That they canna help themsels. It's in their nature to be wi their ain kind, and they'll drap ye in a minute tae get back amang them. And that is why ye huvtae stamp on their very nature – from the minute ye meet them, till the minute they're deid.'

Sammie liked the story of the selkie. But he'd noticed a contradiction which apparently escaped his Instructor. There had been a male and female selkie living together. That was what the woman had run away to rejoin, not a community of Amazons like in the City. That was a whole other kettle of fish-people, you might say. Voluntary cohabitation.

The door of his room clanged open, and he saw the woolly caps and camouflaged fatigues of two Commandos. The gas light glittered dully on their big boots and the butts of their revolvers. Their faces, as ever, were smeared with boot polish.

'Come on, son. It's your turn wi the wumman.'

II

On the way down the dimly-lit tenement stairs, Sammie realised he recognised the bigger of the two Commandos flanking
him.

'Airchie, is that you?'

'Aye, Sammie, it's me. Now shut up, or Deck'll huvtae
report us.'

'Can we no even talk?'

Airchie had been in the class two years above Sammie. He
had befriended him, for no reason that Sammie could discern,
when the bullying had been very bad. He was a tough lad with
a reputation. Everyone had known he would go straight into
the Commandos: he had no need of a 'smart' pal like Sammie.
He realised eventually it was because Airchie was 'smart' himself, a witty person whose immediate peers couldn't even
follow his jokes, let alone talk to him.

The beatings had ceased immediately and Sammie had had
a blessed few months outside his head with someone real to
talk to. Then the rumours about Airchie being a poofter had
started, and they had to avoid each other. Sammie went back
to the round of verbal and physical abuse, his only memento
being the new curse of 'bumchum'. Now Airchie was actually
there with him, on his way to the woman. He knew there was
no way round what was going to happen, but it was nice to
have a friendly face, even one smeared with boot-polish.

'Dye waant tae talk tae the laddie, Airchie?' The other
Commando sounded sympathetic. 'I'll no say onything if ye're
quick.'

'Right. Listen Sammie, ye huvtae shag her.'

'What? They don't tell ye that. Nobody telt me that! They
said it wid be alright if I was jist nasty tae her.'

'Aye, I know. But that's what they expect a real man tae
do. It's how ye get intae the Commandos.'

'And if I don't?'

'It's how ye get intae hot shit.'

'He's no kiddin ye son, ye go on the Black List.'

The Black List meant that you were a non-citizen. You
would be housed in areas only nominally protected by patrols

from the Amazons. Your rations were severely limited. You couldn't get promoted. The Black List was effectively a means of population control. It didn't officially exist – this was a democracy, after all: all men were born equal – but those on the Black List simply didn't live as long.

The two Commandos marched him along a pitch-dark street between two rows of identical tenements. All the lights were out: you could just see the dim shapes of the buildings against the starless cloudy sky. At the end of the street they went up to the door of the pub and showed their ID cards to the policeman on duty. He glanced briefly at the boy and unlocked the door. Then they were in.

The pub was painted brown throughout. At the chest level the dark brown became a yellowy-brown, and the gas mantles brought the tone up to the yellowy-white here and there – but the furniture, floorboards, beer and customers all echoed the same loamy hue. In the mirrors behind the bar, Sammie watched himself approach: a small pinch-faced boy between burly men. The Commandos' eyes blinked whitely in the light.

'Three pints and a short for the lad. It's his Stag Night,' the other Commando said to the barman, who gave Sammie the same perfunctory glance as the policeman, before moving off to fulfil their order. A dirty little man with his hair standing off his head at an odd angle slid along the bar towards them.

'Hey, gee her wan i the mooth fae me!' he said.

'Fuck off granda,' said Airchie. 'The lad's entitled to get pished withoot interference from the like o you.'

'Aye,' said the other Commando. 'Jist coz you couldna get it up.'

'Awright, awright,' said the little man, clearly surprised that the Commandos were attacking him. He slid back along the bar with his eyebrows raised. It looked to Sammie as though the man's elbow ran along a small tram-line. The drinks came and he downed the whisky.

'Drink up: that's yir best plan,' Airchie said out of the corner of his mouth, from which Sammie understood he would not be addressed directly whilst in public.

'I mind when there were proper marriages, instead o aabody interferin atween a man and his wife,' muttered the old man. At this, the barman took his half pint away from him and poured it away. The little man got up and paced up and down a little in frustration, before going out. Sammie followed all this in the mirror while he finished his first pint. Airchie ordered another round.

Half and hour later Airchie and the other Commando took turns to go to the toilet, then checked Sammie's alcohol level with a small breathalyser, and pronounced him ready to proceed. He asked to go to the toilet as well, and Airchie accompanied him.

'Can ye no let me go, Airchie?' he pleaded at the streaming urinal.

'We've got tae deliver ye or we get it. Can ye no force yirsel, Sammie man?'

'Aye I can force mysel tae be hard and nasty. I might even be up tae a clip roond the lug. But I cannae shag her. I mean, I've no trainin.'

'Ye're no supposed tae need trainin ye bampot,' hissed Airchie. Noo come on. Deck's stretchin it for us aaready.'

'Airchie,' Sammie whispered, as he did himself up, 'did you do it?'

Airchie grabbed him by the arm and pushed him at the door, glaring past him at the frosted glass: 'Of course I fuckin did it.'

III

The room was set out like an ordinary sitting room. A small table in front of the fireplace was laid for tea. The kitchen sink was to his right, with a single window. To his left was the little bed, squashed into a recess behind the door. There were two armchairs pulled up to the table. By one of them, the one nearest the sink, was a pair of men's slippers. Over by the sink, wearing a peenie and with her hair up in a scarf, was the woman.

He forced himself not to look directly at her as he headed for 'his' chair and muttered gruffly, 'Whaur's ma tea?'

'What?' she said, and he realised he'd scarcely spoken above a whisper. The room was spinning a bit from all the whisky and he wanted to go to the toilet again already.

'Christ it's hot in here.'

'The last wan made me heap up the fire so's he could...' her voice trailed off helplessly. He noticed that an ornament from the mantelpiece was lying in the fireplace. It was a boy in eighteenth-century dress: brown of course. The head had been crushed by someone's foot. He picked it up and twiddled it in his hands.

'I'm actually hungry, if ye can believe that.'

She eyed him with suspicion, and opened the small oven. Using a dish-towel as an oven glove, she lifted out a glass plate with dried-up potatoes and a stew of some kind on it.

'I hope you're no going tae drag this out,' she said shortly.

He sat at the table, standing the headless boy next to the salt and pepper.

'Jist bring me ma bloody tea, please.'

When she was sitting opposite him he snatched a look. Nothing special. Mousy hair and a turned-up nose. A little round of lipstick over thin lips, probably applied by someone else, and a bruise on her right cheek, certainly applied by someone else. He couldn't see the colour of her eyes, if they had one. She looked a little older than him.

'Are you an Amazon?' he asked, chewing on the overdone lumps of meat.

'Are you stupid?' she retorted. 'Of course I'm no a bloody Amazon. Those bitches dinna let themsels be taken alive. They'd slit ma throat as soon as look at me, jist for being here.'

'So what did you do, before this I mean?'

'You're dead set on blowing this, aren't ye?' she whispered at him. 'Listen, I'll do ye a favour, pal. Jist cut the chat and get haud o ma airm. I'll do a bit yellin for the camera and we'll get this over and done wi.'

Sammie spoke very clearly and distinctly, so that everyone could hear him. 'You know what, dear? I don't feel like it the night. I don't feel like it at aa.'

The woman gave him a long hard look, then shrugged. 'It's your funeral.'

'That stew wiz delicious, HEN,' Sammie continued, in the same tone as before. 'I think I'll jist settle doon wi a paper afore the fire and huv a wee cuppie tea.'

The woman gave a short laugh at this. 'Anything you say, sunshine,' she said, getting up to clear the table. 'Ye've got balls anyway, I'll say that fur ye,' she hissed, out of the side of her mouth.

Sammie made himself comfortable before the fire and contemplated this compliment, the first he had ever received from a woman. He imagined three balls, big and brassy, like a pawnbroker's sign. The first two were just functional, but the third was a testicle of courage, a gonad of valour, a ball of bravery.

They should be bursting in at any moment now, he thought. He could imagine the look of disappointment on Airchie's face. Would Deck feel obliged to report their conversation? Would they punish the woman in some way? He felt beyond responsibility in this matter. He had been presented with a problem, and this was his solution. Take it or leave it. The woman came over with his tea.

'Huv you ever heard the story o the selkie bride?' he asked her.

'Geezabreak, darlin,' she replied, sitting down opposite with her own cup of tea, and eyeing the door nervously.

'Naw, mebbe not. Dye ken if there's a bog oot there?'

'Christ I don't know, there might be one on the stairs.'

Sammie decided he couldn't wait. He tentatively tried the door and found it unlocked, then crept down the stairs in the dark. Where the mid-stairs lavatory should be he found a small brightly-lit chamber containing a TV monitor, a desk, and three bodies. They had all had their throats cut and their genitalia mutilated. Sammie smiled faintly at Airchie's corpse and tried to shut his friend's eyes.

On the screen he could see the woman sitting, smoking furtively and drumming her fingers on the table. The Amazons had clearly been watching them. Sammie realised that, contrary to policy, they'd let him and the woman live. There was a bucket in the corner and he pissed into it, inadvertently splashing the sleeve of the third man, who he didn't know. Then he went back upstairs.

He paused on the threshold of the little flat and smiled at the woman. This felt unconvincing, but he was sure a smile was appropriate, as it had been for Airchie.

'Looks like the selkies have been,' he said. She gaped at him, uncomprehendingly.

'Never mind,' he sighed. 'The guards are deid. If ye want tae mak a break fur it ye'd better get going.'

Brian Johnstone

JOHN KNOX'S RECIPE FOR SALVATION

Ingredients

1   large jar of best guilt extract
6   slices of duty, thick cut
A   cupful of conviction
4   grains of happiness, fine ground
½ a cold heart, diced
Zest of sanctimoniousness
A pinch of pleasure, family variety
Self-denial, to taste

Method

Blend the conviction with the guilt
to produce a thick syrup.
Put to one side.

Reduce the pleasure
Over a fast flame.
Sprinkle on the preferred quantity
of self denial,
and stir until blended.

At this stage
add the happiness,
taking care not to overheat.

Now fold this mixture
into the syrup of guilt
and spread thickly
on the slices of duty.
Roll same round the cold heart
and mould to the desired shape.

Garnish with sanctimoniousness
and bake in a hot oven
for several eternities.

Lynn Jolly

SCUNNURD

Ah'm fed up
wi' a' this Scottish shite.
Kaylies an' hillwalkin'
an' a' that Gaylik stuff
oan thi telly.

Ah'm tellin' ye
ah'd rither huv a nite
it thi video.
The weans in bed an' him oot.
Me wi' a boatla Bacardi
an' a cana Coke.

Mibbe ah'm jis no patriotic.
Ah've nivvur bin boathurd.
Ah've aye wahnted tae travl.
Ah've aye hid a wee noashin
fur India,
bit tae be honest
anythin' Scottish gies me the boke.

A. L. Kennedy

A MEDITATION UPON PENGUINS

Of those who look upon the world of wonders, of those who would see miracles and light, how many have bid their gaze seek out the penguin? And yet did they all; philosophers, warriors, saints; but occupy themselves a little moment in the study of this paragon of birds would not their labours flourish, enriched a thousand times and then a thousand?

Reader, I beg your patience, I beg this fragment from the time which makes your life that I might reveal some shadow of the penguin's glory and the good wisdom of its Path. Trust in me as you would trust a penguin – for who in the deep honesty of his heart may ever say he was betrayed by any penguin – and surely, even this selfless giving of your time and trust bears us an example and first step upon the Path. **Without time for their observation and trust to bring them forth there can come no miracles.** Not with the aid of all the penguins on earth.

It may be a man will cry out, 'But what am I to the penguin and what is the penguin to me?' My answer is as simple as rain: it falls straight. Perhaps you may feel you are distant from the penguin, does this mean you can take no delight in it? When your love is separated from you and in another place, will you love her no more? When you know the stars are untold miles away and not painted on a close roof of a sky, will they cease to glimmer and give joy? **Is it not the duty of any living thing to have place in its heart for any other living thing, be it the worm turning in the earth, or the prisoner in his chains?**

Is there not a further lesson borne by the joyful, Southern bird for our race, the Scots? May we, a people at once above and below all other peoples, not learn that there is a place for us in the great sea of humanity, that we may dive and mingle in it and still not be lost. Remember, like the penguin, may not a Scot be welcome anywhere?

Here, we may also learn that **good things may be sought out with the generous assistance of reflection.** If a man seeks to be near a penguin, he may transport himself across the globe to sit with one on the great ice. Or he may go to the zoo and find one there. He may judge for himself which is the more simple task.

As to the presence of an indissoluble relation between humanity and the penguin, I leave my reader's sure judgement and measured reflection to sift out the truth. As we know, **sure and sifted measurement, measured and sifted sureness and surely measuring siftness all bring on truth.**

Now perhaps a woman may ask, 'How can there be untold wonders concealed in what is, after all, a short and comical, fishy bird?' My answer is short as the penguin itself. **Wonders there are.**

For is not the penguin a bird and yet does it not fly in water not in air, teaching us that **all is possible?** Even for a Scot.

We may see how will and water have smoothed and narrowed the natural feathers of a bird into the almost fur of a penguin, clothing it perfectly against the snow and tempests of its chosen home. The feet of the penguin, though forever naked against such terrible things as icebergs and the bitterness of cold, salt sea, never trouble it for a moment, so fitted are they for their purpose. How equally fit are its wings for swimming, its beak for fishing, its bright eye for discerning white across white. Thus the penguin teaches us of the full rightness and kindness of our world. Deny your relatives, your teachers, the queer twist in your stomach when you wake with the dawn, inexcusably alive – **even to us, the world may be kind.**

And the penguin will also show us, a wandering race, that to stray in arrogance beyond our native place may bring us griefs we never dreamed of. Imagine, reader, the penguin's torment if it was, all at once, arboreally inclined; its pitiful scrambles at mighty trunks, its patterings off leafy branches. What would become of the penguin lost in forests, or indeed, in the rasp and wither of Ghobi sands? Before we ourselves begin such momentous movements and translations we must be sure to equip ourselves for that which may reasonably befall. Preparedness is all. **A penguin with a rope and crampons may climb a tree.**

And is there not a special message for all in the very snows that hem about the penguin? Are we not very specially conjoined with the noble creature in choosing, like it, to live somewhere both movingly picturesque and tragically rich in rheumatic and sinus complaints? Let our nation take pride not in wealth or dominion, but in this.

We may also remember the penguin has no money, neither clothing, nor true shelter and yet it stands proud. **Who has ever seen the penguin stoop?** But, Sir, remember also that men and women, though bound in their souls with a sympathy for the penguin, are not themselves in any way penguins, though many have mistaken them for such. Despite the actions and assertions of many otherwise excellent minds, we must say, 'A woman or a man may not survive, even in soft grass and gentle sun, without the benefit of shelter, food and money. Without even the natural dignity we may observe in the deportment of our treasured beast, a simple human being may fade and die.' Good reader, let not this common error cloud your thought. **A person is not a penguin and cannot be made so.**

Yet may we not aspire to the penguin's joy? Have we not seen it slip with its fellows down its icy slides to bob in the sea, then gaily scramble up to slip again? It will clatter beaks and run in the wind with a light heart. **A heart as light as the penguin's is a thing to be wished for.** And be mindful that this light heart is sustained not by the staple diet of the Scot – the potato, the oat and the fish – but by the staple diet of the penguin – fish alone. **A light heart on only fish.** This, too, is possible, but we may be proud that, despite the lightness and satisfaction of its wintery life and plain fare, the penguin may be seen across the globe from Spain to California in zoological gardens where it may taste the luxury of sun, hail observing humanity and yet still take pleasure in the simplicity of fish. This is the balance constantly maintained within the penguin. **Luxury and simplicity – we may have both.**

But the penguin does not give us pride in balance without humility and right gratitude. Even the littlest child cannot be insensible to a fitting humility when it breaks the simplest egg at breakfast time and then considers that this very egg might have brought forth a whole, new penguin; bold and free. Perhaps the egg had, in reality, only hidden the start of a chicken or duck – **we know the potential is all.** Equally, we may have gratitude that we have not been born a chicken or duck, nor yet boiled to make a breakfast. It is a sad and shameful fact that men have fed upon penguins in dark hours. We should be grateful that penguins have never been moved to

feed upon men. We should be humbled by our former wicked-
ness and determined that we shall be vigilant to prevent the
return of any trace of like abominations. As the Penguin Path
will often remind us, **mind what you eat.**

Consider an instant, reader, the land of the penguin; the
white, flat white of the penguin's home. Consider now the col-
oration of the penguin itself. 'How can it be that the penguin
is both white and black?' a seeker on the path may inwardly
ask. 'What may this signify?'

Here is a nice confusion. Surely like the polar bear, like
milk, the penguin should be wholly white that it might be
rendered safely invisible in its cold surrounds. But no. Things
are quite otherwise and they are so with a purpose. There is a
lesson here on the Path; perhaps the hardest lesson of them all.

Notice that if the penguin should lie upon its face, turning
its back upon the whole arc of the world, only the blackness
of its feathers may be seen, marking out the glorious bird,
exposing it entirely to foes of every kind. And yet, should the
penguin lie upon its back, bearing its vital organs and the red
tenderness of its heart to all that come, then is the whiteness of
its belly feathers lost in the whiteness of the snow. Thus does
the penguin, in embracing Nature, find itself protected by that
very Nature and gentle Power which surrounds it. **Embrace
life freely, Scot, and see how freely it returns your favour.**
Being ever mindful that a penguin does not often lie down, in
either direction.

Oh, reader, think of the Southern winds in the penguin's
feathers: that sound we may never hear, but may imagine.
Know that there is nothing we may not learn, in putting ourselves within the triangular web prints of the noble and
courageous penguin. What goodness and example may we not
find there? Name me the penguin which has ever burned down
a listed building by carelessly smoking in bed? Point me out
the mocker of elderly ladies, the jumper of queues, the giver of
previously sucked boiled sweets to little children who ever was
revealed to be a penguin. What war has a penguin started?
What excellent new plan for economic reformation has ever
been imposed by any penguin?

Think. Who would die for a penguin, kill for a penguin,
offer a penguin their vote? No one. And is this not the finest
and last lesson on the Path? It is indeed. Join with me, reader,
in the fervent hope that our rich and our powerful, our leaders

and our led, our elected and our despots might imitate the virtues of the penguin. Let none die or kill or vote for any one of them. Lift up your cries that the penguin; the obscure, the fishy, the mocked; the shorter than average penguin might become the phoenix of all lands. And let us begin the Path here. Let fly the Penguin Rampant! Let fly all!

Gordon Legge

STUCKNESS

All I ever think about is death – the great big nothing. I rip sheets. I punch walls. I scream under my breath.

The end of my fucking brain, man. Tch.

I'm advised not to worry about it, happens to everybody. Better still, don't even think about it. Good idea. Doesn't work, though, does it?

We're not talking pain here – we're talking that which I am, ceasing to be. Not the meaning of life, just me.

I got a bottle of plonk and a box of Roses, gathered up my notes and calculations and went next door to see Grant, Tracey and the kids. It was time I talked about this.

My audience was captivated as I explained evolution ('millions and millions of this'), nature ('millions and millions of that') and the mechanics of the human body ('the internal telly'). I was away with myself. Grant, Tracey and the kids strove to make points but I never let them.

I showed them my calculations. How I'd worked out the numbers of individual species and how they were always changing. Then I showed how the overall total of 'existors' remained as near as damn-it constant. For years this had led me to give credence to the reincarnation trip. I laughed the laugh of a tired man then took a slug of wine and a hazelnut whirl. I asked if anybody could recall ever having been a Patagonian jumping frog that went by the name of Enrico. Grant, Tracy and the kids gave this some serious consideration before a collective shake of the head indicated the negative. Exactly. This is all we get and we're all going to die.

It was time to dismiss God. I got out my research. Many observers believed that there had once been a God but that he was now dead. Well stands to reason, bozos. My audience laughed nervously. I shook my head. There was never a God. Never. I produced the proof. Pages of unanswered prayers, blank tapes which He was supposed to have left messages on and, most importantly, the two biggies – that life was shitty and the complete and utter failure of my brain to believe.

There was a pause then I asked did anybody want to believe in God. I asked for a show of hands. None, not a pinky. I gave them a lead and raised mine. I could sense the relief as they in turn raised theirs.

You'll never understand anything unless you understand infinity. Something that goes on and on for ever (space and time) produced something that probably doesn't (me). Infinity never ends – and here's the one everybody forgets – and it never ever even started. I'm shivering, trembling and shaking at this bit. I call it the realisation. I got out my piece of paper with the biggest number I could think of. Years and years of calculations had gone into that. Years of them. I handed the paper over and it was duly passed round. Grant, Tracey and the kids were impressed. The paper was returned to me. I got my pencil out and added a five to the end of the number. From the reaction you'd have thought I'd stabbed a baby's heart. It gets folk like that. I ripped the paper up. All that work, I just ripped it up.

Other than the great big nothing infinity is the only thing that freaks me out.

That was it. There's me, drained, my life's work disproved, dismissed and destroyed. For all their earlier attempted inter-ruptions Grant, Tracey and the kids just sat there, silent, like anyone else would.

Suddenly, one of the kids made to say something. He bot-tled it, though, and sat back.

Maybe it was the wine, maybe it was the Roses, I don't know, but my eternal piece of mind rested on what this bespectacled kid with the lime-green shell-suit had to say for himself. No more jumping up and down. No more mumbling in the street. No more staring through strangers.

By Christ, I was excited. My heart was pounding, my palms were sweating – I was covered in wee tingly bits. I got down on my hands and knees and begged him to share his thoughts.

Finally, he spoke. 'Well,' he said. 'What it is is... do you no think kangaroos are right weird looking bastards?'

Douglas Lipton

THE WATERSHED

(Ack. MJW)

This is the wettest, saddest place in Scotland.
'This is the Watershed' – reads tidy graffiti
on the metal wall of a labourers' hut,
in which you stand, awkward as a dromedary,
with gear on your back, in the middle
of somewhere that is a far, far cry
– and a long day's trek through treeless bog –
from anywhere in Scotland. 'This is
the Watershed' – beside an ugly river.
Forbidden its course by an iron sluice
and a rubble of regretted decisions,
it hacks its way through a history
of turf and peat, slanching off great ox-slabs
with spatters of foxglove and lousewort for blood.

Your eyes slide down the wall of this workmen's shed,
where lamenting Jacobites mourn their way,
stanza by stanza adoringly over the zinc,
crying the loss of something elusive
– a vagrant, more glamorous in flight
than in any advance, bobbing about the bogpools,
the Bonnie Moorhen of fond memory
which sings of its like again and again,
more inclined to defeat than to victory.

Below this, near your blood-stopped elbow,
the translated poet refutes the worth
of any moon of paradise
without Blaven. And the poet's very island
crouches, circumscribed indelibly
like childhood memory – with a scribbled
umbilicus attaching it to Scotland.
You ask which way does the succour flow?
The mainland, drawn, for all the world,
as a huddled female, holds to herself
herself, wincing at some windblown quip
on women in the beholder's eye.

As your head cricks on a body, able neither
to sit nor stand,you begin to imagine
the hardbitten man whose work it is
to come here on days that smirr with midges
and fester with clegs, in the pub the night before,
where his friends will have said, 'The Watershed
tomorrow?' – And his reply, from a tumbler
of fumes: the briefest guttural syllable
known to man, the incised and half-chewed
Scottish 'Aye', saying all there is to be said
with a poignancy unmatched by many finer
words, carelessly or lovingly written on walls.

Brian McCabe

NOT ABOUT THE KIDS

He could just remember the apples and oranges careering around the kitchen. And the grapes – that's right, he'd just bought those grapes in the afternoon. He'd picked up a bunch of them in the fruit shop and felt their luxurious weight in his hand, half wondering if they could really afford them, what with being unemployed, and half thinking that the kids hardly ever got grapes. The way they'd scattered all over the floor – ricocheting around the kitchen like the beads of a broken necklace! In his anger he'd scooped the fruitbowl off the table and, in one sweeping movement, flung it at the wall. It exploded. Thank Christ the kids hadn't been there. He had to make sense of what had happened, or else here he was, driving through the night with no real clue about why he was here, in the middle of nowhere in Fife.

A light rain was beginning to fall and he switched on the wipers. He stared at the road in front of him. He was driving. He had to keep his mind on the road. It felt like he'd been driving for a long time, for years and years of his life. Now the road seemed to be coming at him out of the night, negotiating him rather than the other way round, as if it was testing him. If he could just concentrate on driving this car along this road, maybe all the other stuff would sort itself out. He'd had a row with his wife and now he was driving. That was all there was to it.

He braked to take a corner and heard the grinding screech of metal on metal. The break-pads needed to be changed months ago. Now the discs would be scuppered. The shocks needed to be replaced as well, and one of the rear coil-springs was broken. Age, the guy at the garage had told him, looking at him, not the car. But he hadn't had the money to go ahead and get the work done there and then. At any moment the broken spring could leap out, and the car collapse on to the rear axle.

It had been something so trivial, of course, some trivial little thing they'd disagreed about, not about the kids but about the housework – the household chores! Ruth had started getting at him about putting the rubbish out – was that how it had *started*? He'd been sitting there at the table, after the communal family meal. Bobby had been obstreperous as usual, throwing his food on the floor, insisting on drinking out of a glass like everyone else, then spilling his juice all over the table. Emma had been finicky and difficult and the food – an experimental fish curry – hadn't gone down well. She'd interrupted them with needless questions every time they'd tried to speak to each other. There had been a bottle of wine – his idea, along with the grapes. Ruth had declined the wine wearily, saying it was a waste of money. Maybe it had started with the wine, with the waste of money.

And, when the table had been cleared, with Bobby on his knee, popping a grape or two into the boy's mouth, he'd been aware of Ruth making more of a thing of doing the dishes than usual. The plates were crashing and colliding in the sink and she was smashing handfuls of cutlery down on the metal draining board. He'd asked her what the fuck was wrong with her. Nothing was wrong with her, she'd said, but in a tone of voice that seethed with resentment. Then she'd started sweeping the kitchen floor and shouting at Emma to get out from under her feet.

When he thought about it now, it came clearer that what he'd been trying to do was to woo her, but he'd tried to include the kids, when what was needed was not about the kids. What was needed was something else. And it was as if she held him responsible for trying but failing, as if the attempt had reminded her of how things would be but were not. The way she'd swept that floor, like some vengeful Cinderella.

Leave it, he'd said, just fucking leave it and I'll do it later on. Then she'd started dealing with the rubbish, tugging that black bag out of the bucket, tying it up so tightly. What was she trying to tell him? That he was neglecting this twice-weekly fucking ritual, normally earmarked as a chore of his in the demarcation of labour between them? She'd deliberately done one of his chores, encroached on his territory, so that she could get at him about it – could this be true?

He'd picked up Bobby and grabbed Emma by the arm and made for the door. Ruth had shouted something at him about the way he was handling the kids. Christ Almighty. He'd shouted back at her: No, this is not about the kids, this has nothing to do with the kids! So he'd removed them from the battlefield, running their bath and putting them in it before returning to wage war with Ruth about the rubbish. He'd tried to take over but she'd resisted and the two of them had ended up having a tug of war with the rubbish bag. It had split and all the food scraps and nappies and tin cans and eggshells had spilled over the floor, the floor she'd just swept. They'd stopped everything then to argue savagely. Then he'd smashed the fruitbowl and stamped out of the house, slamming the door. It was awful, it was desperate. But what was it all about?

He was finding it hard to concentrate on driving. He kept thinking of all the things he should've said but hadn't found the words for, the reasonable, rational things... He came to a bend so sharp that he had to slow down to a crawl to take it. He didn't know this road and it kept surprising him, dipping and rising and twisting into the night unpredictably. He couldn't go back tonight, that was for certain. Maybe this time he wouldn't go back at all, maybe this was it, the final break, and they'd both remember this night like no other night in their lives.

Up ahead, just beyond the range of his dipped headlights, there was some kind of truck. One of its brake lights wasn't working. A truck or a lorry? It was hard to make out on that dark road. Even when he flicked his headlights on full for a moment, it was difficult to determine the exact nature of the vehicle. A loose tarpaulin was roped around the cargo, whatever it was. At every sudden summit, the truck made a lot of noise, as if its various parts had come apart for a second, only to crash back together as the truck roared on into the night. The way it seemed to veer from side to side unpredictably at every bend bothered him. He put his foot on the accelerator. He felt his heartbeat speeding up too. He knew that if Ruth had been in the car with him he wouldn't take the risk – but she wasn't.

Before he could level with the truck he saw, above the dark embankment at the side of the road, the light from an approaching car's headlights, so he braked and pulled back in. The bastard hadn't slowed down to let him pass – hadn't he stepped on it to make sure he couldn't? The approaching car dipped its headlights as it came round the corner. Even so, it dazzled him and he slowed down till it had passed. There was a moment when he could make out nothing but the red brake-light of the truck, dancing around in the night ahead, a taunting spark, then it disappeared. When his eyes had readjusted he saw that he was too far into the middle of the road as he took the bend, so he swung back out. This road was wild. It wasn't so much the blind summits or the hairpin bends, but the stretches in between, where the road wavered and couldn't make up its mind which way to go.

It was a dangerous road. Maybe it didn't go anywhere. He lit a cigarette and tugged open the overflowing ashtray on the dashboard. He'd been smoking too much and there was a sour taste in his mouth that reminded him of nights years ago, when he and Ruth had started up together, when they'd stayed up most of the night and gone to bed at dawn, making love as the birds were singing outside...

He came over a rise and saw the truck there ahead, its one brake light jiggling up and down, its tail-board rattling. It had slowed down. There was a clear stretch ahead. He accelerated and signalled to overtake, but it was taking longer than it should. The truck threw a spray of dirty rainwater over his windscreen and snarled at him as he drew level with it. He could feel the car jogging around on the uneven road. It was a relief to get in front. Even so, the truck-driver had his headlights at full beam and he could see nothing but the glare of them in his mirror. The truck was gaining on him, so he put the foot down again and tried to leave it behind.

A sharp bend in the road came at him and he had to brake hard to get round it. The brakes screeched. The car skidded and swung too far into the side of the road and scraped noisily against the barrier beneath the sign with the chevrons. At the same moment he was dazzled by the headlights of an oncoming car and he raised his right hand to shield his eyes, trying to right the wheel with his left hand. The other car roared past blaring its horn.

He went on driving, but his heart was hammering and he could feel his hands and his arms shaking. He had to stop somewhere as soon as possible.

As if the road had taken this decision, it wound downwards and showed him a speed-limit sign and the nameplate of a village he'd never heard of. He slowed down until he saw a pub just off the main street, then pulled over and waited till the truck roared past. It was just a truck, moving something from somewhere to somewhere else in the night. He put his hand to his head, pressing his thumb and his forefinger into his eyelids, and he sat like this for a moment before switching off the engine and the lights.

There were only a few people in the pub and he felt conspicuous as he walked to the bar. He was a stranger, and they didn't often get strangers here. They stared at him with hostile curiosity. Some of them seemed to dismiss him quickly, as if they knew he was from the city and had just had a row with his wife.

The barman took too long to serve him. He was serving somebody else but taking his time about it, having a conversation with some of the men sitting round the bar. Apparently they were talking about birds, birds they found living in the eaves of their houses. One man was maintaining that when swifts made their nests they used their spit to hold them together, and that swift's spit was the main ingredient in bird's-nest soup.

He ordered a double and asked if there was a telephone. The barman pointed to the door that led to the toilets. He took his drink to a table by the window and drank half of it and smoked a cigarette. He thought about what he should say to her.

Ruth, it was the way you swept the floor.

Ruth, I demand custody of the kids.

Ruth, I think you should have custody of the kids. They can come to me half the week and stay with you the other half.

Ruth, we need to talk. Not about the kids. About us. What's happening to *us*, Ruth?

He looked at the only woman in the bar, as if this might help him to think of what he should say to his wife. She was sitting on a high stool up at the bar, next to a man – her husband? She wore a tailored leather jacket, the collar of which she held between her finger and thumb to illustrate her point. The man shook his head, raised his eyebrows wearily and slouched on his stool, over which he'd slung his nylon jerkin. They seemed a sad couple, trapped in their coupledom. But maybe they weren't a couple at all. And if they were a couple – what did that mean, exactly, when you got down to it?

The others sitting at the bar all seemed to know each other, though some wore muddied work boots and dungarees, others sports jackets or suits. Over in the far corner, two younger men in jeans and tee-shirts were playing pool and listening to the juke-box.

He took his drink and his cigarettes out to the telephone with him.

It rang and rang. Had she unplugged the phone? Eventually she answered:

– It's me.

– Oh.

– Sorry about the fruitbowl.

– So am I – not just about the fruitbowl.

– I know it isn't just about the fruitbowl. I'll get you another one exactly the same.

– Like hell you will. It was an antique.

– I know, I know, it's irreplaceable. I'm sorry. The thing is, I was angry.

– You were angry. Right. That explains everything, doesn't it? You were angry so you threw the fruitbowl at the wall. If the kids had been there –

– They weren't. I made sure of that.

– They could have been. Anyway *I* was there.

He apologised again then waited until she spoke.

– Where are you?

– Fife.

– What the hell are you doing in Fife?

– I don't know, I drove here.

– You must be out of your mind.

– I am. I am totally out of my mind.

– You're drunk.

– No, not yet.

– You're driving.

– That's right. I'm driving.

– You must be crazy.

– At this moment, you're right, I am completely crazy.

She didn't reply to that. He waited a minute, then he said:

– What's it about?

– What?

– All this. What's it all about?

– What do you think it's all about?

– That's what I'm asking you.

She sighed with fatigue and said wearily that she didn't know. He was glad she didn't. That gave him the initiative:

– It's something to do with me losing my job, isn't it?

– No. Of course not.

– I'm around the house too much. We're with each other all the time. I mean, sometimes a person has to go away just so that they can come back.

– Don't come back. Not tonight.

– Don't worry, I won't.

– I don't want to talk anymore. I'm tired, I want to go to bed.

– I'll tell you a bed-time story, then. Once upon a time, there was a boy and a girl, and they fell madly in love with each other. But they were young, just kids –

– I've heard this story before.

– Not this one, Ruth, this one is not about us, this one is about these kids, these kids who fell madly in love. In those days, Ruth, it was as simple as that. We're talking about a time when people went out with each other for a month, if it was serious. But these kids are so in love they manage to go on for a year, more than a year... That gives you some idea how serious about each other they are. But, as I was saying, they're young, too young to really know how to *go on* being in love, if you know what I mean, and after a while something has to happen.

The pips sounded, and he hurriedly pulled a handful of coins from his pocket, dumped them on the shelf and searched among them for a ten pence. He found one and put it in just as they were about to be cut off.

– Ruth? Are you still there?

– What's the point of all this?

– So, and this is the sad bit of the story, there comes a point when the boy begins to feel restless, he feels the need for change... He's changing anyway, he's growing up, and the whole world is changing round about him. And so one night, out of the blue, the boy tells the girl he wants to finish with her. So they split up. Some time passes. The boy is totally miserable without the girl, but he is alone. He's himself and only himself. Then he goes back to her, and she takes him back with open arms. And they go on together again, pretty much as before except that everything has changed. In fact, nothing is ever quite the same after that brief separation. And soon the girl begins to feel restless, she feels the need for change...

– You got what you deserved. What d'you want, sympathy?

All I'm saying is sometimes people need the threat of separation, I mean so they can go on. The threat has to be real. But as soon as it is real it will never go away, it will always be there. D'you know what I'm saying, Ruth?

– You're saying it's time to split up.

– I never said that.

Maybe we should.

– Just remember it was you who suggested it first.

– What does it matter who suggests it first?

– It matters. Everything matters.

– Don't sound so gloomy about it.

– How should I sound – cheerful?

– I'm not saying that.

– What are you saying?

– I'm not saying anything.

– Well, why not? Are we communicating with each other here or what?

– I'm tired of communicating. We can communicate tomorrow.

– What about tomorrow?

But he could feel her attention slipping away from him. He tried to hold it.

– Are the kids okay?

– They're asleep, if that's what you mean.

– That isn't what I mean.

– What do you mean then?

– I mean are they okay? Come on, you know what I mean.

– They're okay, yes.

– Christ Ruth, I was trying tonight. I tried with the meal, I tried with the kids, I tried with us...

– I know you tried. D'you think I haven't been trying? I'm always trying. Maybe that's the problem. Maybe it's just too much effort.

– You sound exhausted, Ruth.

– I am. My period's come.

– D'you think that had something to do with it?

– How do I know? Maybe, maybe not.

The pips went. He tried to tell her that he'd call her again in the morning, but he was cut off.

He took his drink back to the bar, finished it and ordered another. No one seemed to pay him any attention now, and they had become a meaningless blur to him. He didn't want to look at them, so he sat down in a chair that faced the window. He stared at his distorted image reflected in the marbled glass, and when he moved his head a little, his features disintegrated horribly.

Her period? Maybe, maybe not. But what, really, had happened? Maybe nothing had really happened. Maybe the threat was all that was needed. But then, maybe what he'd said to her was true: once the threat was there, it would never really go away.

If she could be here with him now... but all that lay ahead was the night, a night spent alone, in a bed-and-breakfast in Fife. The utter pointlessness of it made him bang his glass down on the table as he finished his drink. Someone laughed at the bar, and he thought he heard a low-toned comment from one of the tables. He closed his eyes and listened. The clack of the pool balls, the music from the juke box, the voices – all the noises in the bar seemed to swell inside him and engulf him, until he felt adrift in the world. He had to get out.

It had stopped raining, and the night was cool and clear. He walked to the car but didn't get in. He leaned against it and looked along the dark street of the village, at the haphazard silhouette of the rooftops. He imagined the swifts in the eaves, their nests being held together by spit, their eggs... It reminded him vaguely of his childhood, although he had never lived in such a place.

TRANSLATION

C. MacKenzie

(From Burns' – 'To a Louse')

ORAN NA MIALL

Ud! Càit' bheil dùil riut, 'chulaidh-sgràth thu
'S do ladarnas a' ceil do nàire;
Air m' fhacal shin! 's glan nì thu stàrachd
Thar sròl is sìoda
Ged's cìnnt na leithid sin a dh'àite
Gur lom do dhìneir.

A chreutair shnàgach, ghrànnda, chaca
Cha taobh riut aon chuid naomh na peacach;
Ag ionaltradh air òigh cho tlachdmhor
An gabh thu ort e?
Bi tarruing, 's lorg dho dhiot air craiceann
Diol-déirc na gorta.

Thoir ort! 's an dosan na diol-déirce
Bi cleasachd 'sin am luib na spreidhe
A bhuineas dhuit, dream sùrdail, leumnach
Sluagh tha gun chùnntas.
Nach dèan cìr-mhìn na garbh an treudan
Am feasd a dhùsgadh.

Nis, socair ort, sud thu as fianuis
Fo bhréid na ribein, còs nam biasdan;
Ach feuch a bheil! cha chumar sìor thu
Gu'n toir thu mach e,
Am binnein 's àird air bonaid chiatach
Na maighdinn thlachdmhor.

A Rìgh! nach tus tha aghach, srònach
Do chlosach ghlas cho cruinn ri greòiseid;
O, nach robh agam smior na ròsaid
Na fùdar mairbhteach;
Is mise smùideadh air do thòin dheth
Na dh' fheannadh d' earball.

Ged chithinn thu air currachd caillich
Cha ghabhainn iongnadh; na am falach
'S a léinidh a bhios leth ri balach
Tha robach, sgràthail.
Ach ceannabheairt Lùnardi na caileig!
'S tu chaill do nàire.

A Shìne nis, na bi cho pròiseil
A' nochdadh thall 'sa bhos do bhòidhchead;
Is beag tha dh' fhios agad a bhrònag
An t-astar siùbhlach
Tha bhrùid a' dèanamh, 's càch gu spòrsail
A' cumail sùil oirr'.

Nach tugadh freasdal sùilean chàich dhuinn
A tha 'g ar faicinn mar a thà sinn;
'S e ghleidheadh sinn o iomadh ànnradh
'S o bheachdan dìomhain.
Nach grad bhiodh fearas-mhór 'g ar fàgail
Is riochd na Diadhachd.

D. Maclean

RIGH NA FRITHE

Mur a b'e gu'n do leòn an damh òg a sgairt air post iaruinn
bha e air a bhi a' ruith anns an Dàmhair a' bhliadhna roimhe
seo. Bha e na bu shine na bha a nuallan a' dèanamh de
dh'fhuaim agus is e sin a mheall air an damh eile aig an robh
dùil gu 'n dèanadh e a' chùis air ann a' sabaid.

Mar a thachair anns an t-sabaid, mharbh an damh seo am
fear eile nuair a ghearr e a sgòrnan le a chabar, ach cha
d'thàinig e fhèin idir as an t-streupa gun uireasbhuidh. Tharr a
chabar fhèin an damh òg anns an fheith-mhòir a bha ann an
cùl-amhaich, agus bha e air a dhroch ghoirteachadh. 'Na
shuidheachadh leònta lorg e àite sàmhach gu h-àrd air a'
bheinn, sin airson ùine, ach mo chreach mhòr thàinig "là-an-
trusaidh" – bha daoine is coin a-mach ann a neart agus
sgrìobadh iadsan gach àrd is ìosal.

Chruinnich gach beathach fèidh o thall 's a-bhos agus thug
iad na buinn dhi air falbh o bheanntan an trusaidh... bha iad
air a leithid fhaicinn mu thràth. 'S ann air còmhnard beag aig
ceann an loch uisge a stad iad agus air m' onair theireadh
neach gu 'm b' ann a' co-labhairt a bha iad mu gu dè a bu
chòir 'dhèanamh a nis.

Bha seann agh mòr nam measg agus rinn ise suas a h-
inntinn gu 'n dèanadh i air ceann a-stigh na frìthe. Bha àite
àraidh ann a' sin a dh'ionnsuidh an robh i a' tighinn gach
geamhradh bho bha i ann an cois a màthar, ach cha d'thàinig i
riamh ann cho tràth seo. Dè a thug air an damh òg, nach robh
air a bhi riamh air talamh ìosal, an t-agh seo a leantail chan eil
fhios, ach lean e i dlùth air a sàil, ceum air cheum.

Nochd an dà bheathach fèidh seo air fàire na h-aonaich a
bha os ceann a' bhaile gun nì a thachairt agus thàinig iad a
nuas beagan a measg nan creagan beaga a bha a' dèanamh
suas aghaidh na h-aonaich.

Bha an aghaidh seo de 'n aonaich air leth cas agus bha sin
a' toirt seallaidh dhaibh air gach nì a ghluaiseadh fad astar
mòr. Shios fodhpa bha am baile beag anns nach robh ach
ceithir croitean le taigh air gach croit. Cha robh an t-agh agus
an damh fada ann am fianuis 'nuair a mhothaich Speireag
dhaibh agus shaoileadh neach gu 'n tigeadh an saoghal a nuas

leis na rinn i de chomhartaich. Cha mhòr nach do chuir comhartaich na h-amhaig' an damh as a rian, ach mu 'n robh mionaid na h-uarach seachad bha an cu-beag a' gabhail barrachd ùidh ann an cat geal an taighe na bha e anns an dà choigreach a bha air tighinn far a' mhonaidh.

Bha mòran de nithean ri 'm faicinn agus ri 'n cluinntinn ann a seo a bha annasach agus gu dearbha eagalach, do'n damh, ach mar a chaidh ùine seachad dh'fhàs e cleachdte ri gnothaichean. Chuir an rathad mòr iongnadh air an damh, gus gu 'n do shaoil leis nach b'urrainn neach a bha a' falbh air fhàgail. Bha dùil aige gu'm b'e sneachd' a bha ann an cobhar na mara agus eadhoin an sùragan fhèin a bha a ghnath ri fhaicinn saoil leis gu'm b'e nì a thàinig a nuas anns an fhrois shneachd' a bh'ann.

Dh'fhàs an damh, cuideachd, cleachdte ri mnathan a' bhaile a bha a' cur sgian air an toiseach, gu h-àraidh aig àm an eadraidh. Chluinneadh e Maighread ag eigheach "Trobhad a bhò-ruadh" ri bò nan adharcan crombach agus bha Màiri a ghnàth na h-ualach dha le a duanagan-bleoghainn. Bhiodh Màiri cho tric a' seinn is gu'n robh i air a h-ainmeachadh mar Mairi-ceòl.

Bha an damh òg a ghnath an-fhoiseil agus theireadh an t-agh ris, "Tha thu a' toirt nithean ort fhèin. Carson nach'eil thu a' fuireach faisg air na preasan leis na slatan chabar a tha sin air do cheann. 'S ann air son na coilleadh a thàinig sinne ann a seo an toiseach. Tha tòrr de do dhìon ann a seo an crochadh air fuireach faisg air nì a tha coltach riut fhèin."

Thug an Nollaig deuchainn do'n damh. Bha e fhèin agus na bhiodh timchioll air riamh a' coimhead air an oidhche mar am fior charaid. 'S ann innte a bha an dìon agus am beathachadh agus mar sin bha iad saorsnail ann an uairean an dorchadais.

Bha an Nollaig eadardhealaichte ris gach fèin-fhiosrachadh a bha aig an damh. Eadar eilearadh dhaoine, ceòl is eigheach, danns' air na drochaidean fiodha agus soluis cha mhòr nach do chaill an damh a chiall. 'S e an t-agh a-ris a chuir ceart e, ann a seo. "Thèid seo seachad," theireadh i ris, "'S fhiach an an-fhois seo cur suas leis airson blàths an àite," agus mar a thubhairt, b'fhìor, chaidh gach fuaim is eile seachad.

'Nuair a thàinig an cur-shneachda aig a' bhliadhn-ùir chuir e a' chlach-mhullaich air na choinnich ris an damh. Cha b'e an cur fhèin no na dh'fhàg e de shneachda air an talamh a rinn an trioblaid, ach greigh mhòr de choigrich fhiadh a thàinig gu fasgadh an aonaich on a' chathadh a bha air a' bheinn. Thionndaidh am feasgar a mach sàmhach agus caran soilleir eadar blàr geal agus sìneadh an latha agus cha robh e neo-àbhaisteach Màiri agus Oighrig fhaicinn aig an tobar.

Cha b'e ceòl no cainnt a ghlac aire an daimh air an fheasgar seo, ach glagadaich uamhasach a rinn Màiri leis na cumain fhalamh. Bha Màiri, le fradharc an t-sulaire a bh'aice co-dhuibh, air mothachadh gu' robh fear-a-ghunna aig an t-sorchan. Nochd an gille òg gu dlùth do na fèidh agus thug iad air falbh, ach ma thug, cha b'ann gu am banais. Chualas a creach – dà urchair air sàil a chèile agus thuit dà agh-sheasg air ball.

Sgap na fèidh an Ear 's an Iar agus cha mhòr nach do stad cridhe an daimh le eagal agus a nuair a sheall an t-agh air thubhairt e rithe, "'S e an droch-àite fhèin, air a leigeil mu sgaoil a tha seo"… ach chiùinich an t-agh e, ag ràdh, "Gabh air do shocair agus na caraich, chan eagal dhuinne. Chan e am beathach as treise is dòcha bhi beò ann a' seo ach am beathach as truaighe. Sin a' chas air am bheil a' bhròg, gu tric, far am bheil daoine, cuiridh iadsan craiceann-tarsuinn air nithean nàdurra fhèin."

Dh'fhan an damh agus an t-agh air an aonaich seachduin an deidh seachduin agus cha do chuir duine dragh orra. Cha chuireadh beathach seach beathach aca lann air sùgh agus mar sin cha robh ùidh aig duine annta.

Bha an t-agh a nis aosda agus air fàs mall ach bha i a' dol mu 'n cuairt gus an d'thainig gaoth an Earraich. Bha a' ghaoth seo fuar, bha i tioram agus cha robh am fasgadh air an aonach leatha a bha air leis a' ghaoith àbhaistich. Còmhla ris gach truaighe 's e àm nan gartan a bh'ann agus air son foghnach-dain do'n agh bhochd, cha robh gun tighinn ach iadsan. Chroch na creutairean beaga neimheil seo iad fhèin ris gach nì ris an robh e buailteach do bheathach sam bith anns an robh fuil bhlàth suathadh.

Bhiodh an gartan ann a' sud ùine nan ùineachan a' feitheamh crochte le a spùirean a-mach airson e fhèin aiseag gu beathach anns an dol seachad. Nuair nach robh e mar sin bha e 'na shìneadh air tom-suidhe nam beathaichean agus a chasan os a cheann, airson e fhèin aiseag chuca. Tha e beò airson fuil agus fuil. Tha poca aige airson an fhuil a ghleidh-eadh agus bheir e à beathach dhith ann an taobh a stigh de dha sheachduin na chumas beò e fad bliadhna.

Ged is meanbh iad, is e seo na creutairean a chuir na tairgnean mu dheireadh ann an ciste an aigh. Ghabh an damh iognadh aon fheasgar nach robh i ag èirigh as a laighe. Ged a bha a' ghrian a' tuiteam gu dian, gu "tìr fo thuinn", cha robh guth aig an agh air èirigh. Bha an damh air a bhi cho tric 'na fhaire nuair nach ruigeadh e a leas is gu 'm b'iomadh uair a thubhairt i ris, "'S tràith a dh'èireas a' fear nach laigh," ach a-nochd chan èireadh ise.

Bha fios aig an damh gu 'n robh suidheachadh ùr ag èirigh suas agus bha seo 'na uallach dha, ach dh'fhan e dlùth dhi fad na h-oidhche. Aig briseadh na fàire dh'innis aiteal beag gaoithe bho thaobh an aigh dha gu'm b'fheàrr dha a chasan a thoirt leis.

Thog an damh ris an aonaich, a' toinneamh 's a' sniomh a shlighe, gus an do ràinig e a mullach. Aon uair eile bha frìth mhòr nam fiadh fosgailte air gach taobh dheth. Bha an samhradh ri tighinn agus bhiodh esan àrd agus saor, bha e a nis air slànachadh gu tur bho uireasbhaidh agus anns na mìosan a bha air thoiseach chuireadh e air cuideam mòr.

Nuair a thainig àm na Dàmhair bha an damh òg seo làn deiseil air a shon. Sheas e air an fhaobhar àrd, ann an ceum nan aighean, a' cur stad orra agus ga 'n cuartachadh dha fhèin. Bha nis an damh òg 'na làn damh agus rinn e dà langan mhòr. Bha fèidh eile mu chuairt, ach cha do cheasnaich aon dhiubh ughdarras – bha an rìgh air a chrùn.

Duncan McLean

THE LIKES OF ME

He was in the workshop putting a new belt on somebody's spin-drier when Craig came through from the frontshop.

Kate's here, said Craig.

Who?

Kate, your wife for fuck's sake, she's through the front.

Gary looked up. Eh...does she want to see me?

What? Craig stared at him. Aye she does, she does want to see you, funnily enough. Jesus! Will I send her in?

No, no. Gary stood up. I'll come through man, otherwise she'll be here all fucking day. Craig nodded and Gary walked past him and out. She was standing near the door of the shop, looking at a dish-washer machine. Gary stopped halfway across the floor. I'm busy, he said, and wiped his hands down the sides of his boiler-suit.

Kate looked up and smiled. Hello, she said.

I'm busy, he said again, so... He looked at her, eyebrows raised.

I've no time either, she said, But I just nipped over, ken, to see if you were okay.

He shrugged.

No, just after me not seeing you this morning and that, ken. You should've woke me, I like to see you before you go off to work.

Aye, well, I kind of woke up early, so I thought I'd just head over here, get stuck in. We've a lot on...

I thought you hadn't slept properly; I was minding that you were waking up with dreams or something...

Dreams?

Aye, what were they all about?

He looked around the shop. I wasn't dreaming, he said.

Aye, you were: you woke me up with them!

Look, for fuck's sake Kate! I'm busy, have you just come here to bug me about fucking dreams I didn't have? I've got to get on!

Gary...

He moved away from her and turned his back to brush some dust off a stand displaying fuses. Aye, he said, I think we'll actually be finishing late the night, we've that much on. So don't keep me tea or nothing; I'll probably just have a pint with Craig when we finish instead.

Oh. Well. Here... She reached inside her coat pocket and pulled out a plastic bag with some sandwiches wrapped up in it. You forgot your piece, she said.

What?

Your dinner, you must've forgot it this morning. I made it up last night; did you not see it lying on the table?

Eh, no.

You'd forget your head, eh?

He sniffed.

She held out the package. Well, here they are; you'll be needing them if you're going to miss your tea.

Chuck them over.

Eh?

He clapped his hands and held them out towards her. Come on for fuck's sake, he said, I'm busy.

She shook her head. You're weird sometimes, she said. She threw the sandwiches across the shop, and they flew over the rows of washing-machines and fridges and cookers and he caught them. Immediately he turned and went through to the workshop.

See you later then, she called after him.

He didn't reply, but stood just inside the workshop door, waiting, till he heard her go out and the shop door closing. Then he hurled the bag of sandwiches across the room, his arm flung hard, and they shot by Craig's head and thudded against the far wall knocking down a calendar with a photo of a topless woman reclining along a chest-freezer on it.

Craig slowly lifted his head. Hassles? he said.

Gary stared at the ground for a moment. He was breathing hard. But when he looked up he was calm. No problem at all, he said and smiled. No problem at all for the likes of me.

He had a quick wash at the sink in the workshop after Craig left, then hung around for another half hour. It was only the back of six, but already dark outside. He locked up the shop and left, walking quickly away and into the centre of town. He slowed to a stop outside a lounge bar and checked his watch: ten to seven. He looked up and down the street and went in.

Standing at the bar was a thin girl with long black hair. He walked up behind her and gave her hair a yank, putting his fingers under the bottom of her short skirt at the same time and pressing them into her backside. She squealed, and turned round to face him, her face red.

You're keen, he said, grinning.

She pushed him away an inch, grinning too. *I'm* keen? she said, her eyes looking over his face, and laughed.

You're early!

Complaining?

Nah' not at all. He looked down the bar, catching the eye of the barman. What're you for?

No, I'll get them, she said. I raided the piggy-bank earlier.

Women's lib, that's what I like to hear. Lager for me, ta.

They got their drinks and went and sat at a table in a far corner away from the juke box and trivia machine.

Cheers! she said.

Cheers!

They drank. He sighed and drank again. Cheers! he said.

Cheers! They took another drink.

Well, he said after a moment, How's your mother's automatic doing?

What?

Still going okay is it?

It should be: you only put it in two days ago!

I just like to check, ken...

Here, I hope we're not going to be talking about electrical goods all night!

Some electrical goods can be quite exciting you know...

Such as?

He frowned, then winked. You know.

No. What?

Come on, you know! He nudged her with his elbow.

Gary, what?

He laughed. Well, if it hadn't've been for your mother needing a new bloody Creda we wouldn't be here, would we?

She laughed. That's true. She looked at him sideways, and laughed again. You're funny, she said.

Christ, you say the nicest things.

No, I just mean funny peculiar that here's me finished my drink three hours ago and you've never went up to get us a new one!

God, you finished already? Hold on. He downed the rest
of his pint. That's what I like to see, he said, A woman who
can hold her drink. He stood up and was away to lift the
glasses, then paused and leant over towards her. Here, he said.

What? she said, looking up at him.

He glanced over his shoulder, then back into her face.
How does a French woman hold her liquor? he whispered.

She raised her eyebrows. How?

By the ears...

She chuckled for a second, eyes closed, then stuck out her
tongue at him, and he turned and headed for the bar, grinning
to himself. When he came back he moved his chair closer to
hers before sitting down.

Are you hungry or something? she said.

What?

Three packets of crisps?

He laughed. Well, eh, I didn't have any dinner, see. Kate
forgot to give me my sandwiches this morning...

She looked at him. Kate? she said, her lips moving slowly,
Is that your wife?

He turned and stared at her, one hand half into a bag of
crisps. Listen, he said, I told you, I did tell you, don't say I
didn't, I told you I was married.

She sighed and looked away. I ken you did, it's not that.
It's just that you never told me her name, ken...

Oh, aye...

I don't mind if you don't, about her; it's just, I'd rather
not talk about her, you know.

Aye, Christ, I'm sorry, we won't. It's a deal: I won't talk
about my wife and you won't talk about your mother, okay?

The girl nodded slowly. Okay, she said, and took a drink.
Mind you, she went on, Why the hell we'd want to talk about
my ma I don't know...

Well if your ma hadn't wanted a new machine...

Aye?

And if she hadn't been off at the hospital getting her paps
X-rayed or something...

Aye?

Well, you wouldn't've been taking the morning off college
to look after your wee baby sister and we wouldn't've met
ever. And we wouldn't be sitting here now getting on barrie.
All thanks to your ma!

She looked at him for a second over the rim of her glass. Here, she said, I thought we weren't going to talk about her.

Sorry, he said, and laughed. He reached his hand out across the table and placed it on top of hers, pressing it down on top of the bags of crisps, the bags crinkling and the crisps inside crunching into pieces.

It was late and the street was dark and almost empty. They stopped in front of the shop door, her turning to face him. She didn't speak, just looked at him for a second, then closed her eyes. He put one hand on her shoulder, the other on the back of her head, and leant over her, pushing her back against the door, kissing her on the mouth. She put her arms around his waist and kissed him back. After half a minute he took a step away and looked at her.

Don't stop, she said.

He looked up and down the street. You want me to go on?

Aye.

In here then, he said, and pulled her away from the door. He stuck his key in the lock then shouldered open the door, making the bell above it ring loudly out and down the quiet street. She nipped inside and he followed immediately after, closing the door behind them with a kick. She grabbed him round the neck and kissed his face, then moved her hands down over his shoulders and pulled his jacket off; it dropped to the floor, sending a pocketful of coins clattering onto the lino and rolling away through the shop, some of them clinking and ringing as they collided with the bases of the machines on display.

She giggled, but he didn't, he just said, Come on, not here. He moved her towards the back of the room, then through the door and into the workshop.

She turned to him again, looking at his face in the stripes of orange light that came from the street lamp outside the barred windows. She took off her coat, then started unbuttoning the neck of her dress.

Wait, he said, looking past her into the half-dark.

She stopped. What's the matter? She frowned. Gary?

He shook his head. Nothing, just... He took a step to one side and pulled a big piece of old curtain-material from around a twin-tub. Saves the paintwork getting bashed in the van, he said, as he flung it on the ground behind her, and pulled it out roughly flat with the toe of his trainer. Then he fell to his knees on the material, took hold of her round the hips and pulled her down after him.

Within seconds most of their clothes were off and he was bent over her sucking hard on her nipples, her with one hand down between his legs, the other amongst the hair on his chest. Then he moved to lie on top of her, ran his tongue down her cheek, leant back slightly, moving her thighs apart with his knees.

Stop, she said.

No, I can't, I can't...

No, but get a thing on before you do anything, a durex, go on, there's a pack in my coat.

But I don't have any!

No, *listen*, I do: the inside pocket of my coat, over there...

Oh Christ... He shauchled over on his knees, trousers tight around his ankles, to where her coat was lying on the floor and lifted it out of the shadows into the barred light from the windows till he found the inside pocket and the packet in its depths. Tearing the wrapping off as he moved, he crawled back towards her, then paused, gazing down at her. Don't look, he said, I feel daft doing this.

She giggled and turned her head away. Hurry up, she said, I'm dying...

Right! He slid himself along her body, shoving inside her as his mouth moved over her chin and onto her mouth, breathing in her breath as he heaved and she dug her nails into his backside pulling him down and in, and he could feel the bump of her hipbones banging on the floor as he pushed and pushed and she pressed against him and he raised his head and rested his brow for a second on the cool metal of the half-dismantled washing machine behind them till his whole body tensed up, went stiff, held for a moment, then shivered and relaxed and he crumpled down on top of her.

Don't stop!

Have to, he said, breathing heavily, That's me done.

Well...don't come out yet. She moved herself underneath him for a few seconds, then suddenly stopped. Okay, she said. Get out before you leak.

He put a hand down and held the condom in place as he came out of her, stood up, and shuffled over to the sink. Then he eased it off and chucked it into the waste-bin there. He picked a mug out of the sink, rinsed it, filled it from the tap and took a long drink.

Christ I'm hot, he said. Do you want a drink?

She didn't answer. He laid the mug back in the sink, then moved over, bending to pick up his tee-shirt and trainers as he went, and stood over her, putting them on. After a second he knelt down beside her. She turned her face away. She was crying. He looked down the length of her body, ran a hand over her ribs where they pressed through the skin.

Don't cry, he said, That was great.

She sniffed. Sorry, she said, but she was still crying.

Here, what's the matter...Miss? Miss? Was it not good for you?

Oh, the earth moved, she said, and laughed a bit, still crying.

Moved? Christ, it was a fucking landslide! He jumped to his feet, and moved around the room, picking up her clothes. He flung the bundle down on the bit of cloth beside her, then finished dressing himself. Come on, he said, We better get moving, it's wearing late.

He leant back for a minute against a cooker and watched her untangling her tights; she was still sniffing, stopping every few seconds to wipe at her eyes. Eh... He looked down. Listen, he said, You have done it before, eh?

She nodded, pulling on her dress.

That's all right then.

Just once, she said. At school.

Oh aye, very good. Sex education, eh? I never got none of that when I was at the school.

She got to her feet, picking up the old curtain, folded it neatly and laid it on top of a machine.

Of course, he went on as she walked past him, heading for the door, There's not much I need to learn on that subject, eh!

Through in the frontshop, she waited for him by the door. He came up beside her. What would your wife do if she found out? she asked.

About tonight? Christ, she'd put my head in a microwave! he said, and laughed.

She opened the shop door and went out onto the pavement. Or your prick in a liquidiser, she said, as he fumbled to fit his key into the lock and close up.

Fuck's sake! He stopped and turned to look at her. What

an idea! A liquidiser? Fuck, you're sick! He shivered. I'll be thinking about that every time I have to look at one now!

Good, she said, and started walking off down the street.

Hold on, he called after her.

She carried on, walking quickly, not waiting for him to catch up.

Iain F. Macleòid

BIASDAN HUILM

Thàinig thu gu socair am follais an oidhche ud
Fo chop agus sàl, a' gàireachdain 's a' fuireachd
Agus reub thu am mionach agus bhris thu bratach
Dòchais agus gaoil eadar na creagan olca, dubha.

Dubh is grànnda le spùirean tiachdaidh, borba
Mar sùil neo-chiontach dàin a' feitheamh le gàire
Cist mhòr, dhorch a dh' òladh pròis agus gaisge
Mar a dh' òlas faileas dorchadas.

Sheas iad air a' chidhe mar bhallet dorch
Agus chunnaic iad an t-isean bochd a' bàthadh
Air a' Chloich dheirg làn fuil agus deòirean
Sàl air gach aghaidh agus do sgiath briste.

Chaidh an t-Eilean a bhriseadh an oidhche ud
A bhàthadh ann am meadhan a' chuain fhuair
A shluig na gaisgich is gaol gun dragh
A' giùlan ar caraidean gu grunnd is fad na h-ùine
         a' gàireachdain
         a' gàireachdain.

THE BEAST OF HOLM

You came quietly into view on that night
Under foam and salt water, laughing and waiting
And you ripped the belly and you broke the banner
Of hope and love between the evil, dark rocks.

Dark with withering, sharp claws
Like the unguilty eye of providence waiting with a smile
A large, black coffin which would drink pride and bravery
Like a shadow drinks blackness.

They stood on the pier like a black ballet
And they watched the poor bird drown
On the red stone full of blood and tears
Salt water on each face and your wing broken.

The island was broken that night
Drowned in the middle of the cold sea
That swallowed our heroes and love without a care
Carrying our friends to the bottom and always
                                     laughing,
                                       laughing.

Claire MacRae

IN THE COUNTRYSIDE

I'm sitting in this room at three o'clock, I close my eyes and think the afternoon. If I hold my breath until the block is hard inside my chest and screw my eyes far back inside my head, it waits for me. See the big field I cross faster than the dog, faster than a deer if I raced one, smell the way into the trees where the ground never dries, even when it's hot like now, further than any.

HEW! ARE YEW IN THE LAND OF THE LIVING?

Not if that means here. You put the blind down because fanny Janet had the sun in her eyes, but I'm out there and you never even saw me go. Your glutty eyes are nae use, might as well be properly blind and sit at home all day.

For GUEDNESS SAKE try and pay attention

You look like you just found something in your hanky. Then you put the smile back on for the rest, there's something nice you want to tell. I bet they can't wait.

The door opens like falling onto the playground that's all white with the sun. Soon as I'm through it I'm running, the sun goes with me on my back, we slam the pavement down, and WATCH WHERE YE'RE GOING EH that was near, that was nearly Shona Fulton's mum that's pregnant like the side of the hoose. Like a big cow, next time I'll headbutt her in the belly. They're all staring, so maybe they never seen anyone run like this. They could never run ever, not even for the bus. I'm supposed to wait for Linda, I remember, but she can get home herself, I'm going back. THUD THUD THUD my feet on the hot ground, past the shop, and they can get out of my way.

I'm out of the village before the bus passes me. See Tommy Boyd's face and hands pressed up flat against the back window, and his tongue like a fat wet slug. Feed him salt and make it dissolve away, hiss.

Stop running.

Missus Magregor said that she got good NYEUSE. See them all look up at our table. Primary seven, there's seven of us too. Five and six at the other tables look up, but she's not meaning them. Can we go early Missus Magregor, with a PLEEZE that's like trying to squeeze out a shite. Here it comes.

> There will be no homework this weekend!
> There will be no HOMEWORK this weekend

which leaves ample time for the SPECIAL STORY you're going to write! Tommy's face that was all puffed up in a grin goes flat, like someone stuck a pin in him to let the air out. But the new girl, I bet she's well chuffed. Missus Magregor's red smiley mouth comes bigger and closer. And the best one – the best story –
Will be READ ALOUD at the summer show!
If she smiles any wider her face will split in half. The new girl is trying to look like she doesn't care, but it's obvious that she's really excited. Her eyes are all stretchy wide like she can already see her mam and dad in Cunningham Hall listening to the whole village listening like twats to their wee girl's story. But she doesn't say anything, she knows better already.

See the long summer evenings... That's what old pricks say. But I do like it though. Light till ten o'clock, stretching the sky forever. The hills over that way lose colour against it, become all ruggy shape against the light. I snake on my belly, one eye on Rocky, the dog, he's kind of brown and lopsided and getting old. All I can smell is the grass, unless I lift my head up and get the smoke, mixed with a dusty smell of dog. I spring to catch him and his hair and smell collide with me, my ears are full of his wet growling, but he won't bite. I take him over the wall (I don't give a fuck why they're DYSTANE DYKES) into the big field where we run. It's not a fair race, but I don't think he minds. Sports day with the schools from Aberdour and Kincraig I make them sick, I make them sweat, if I went. Bare feet I could run and win. But it's like my dad says, it's always one bloody day or other at that place.

God gives everybody their OWN SPECIAL TALENT

Tonight my dad's away somewhere, thank fuck. Kirsty cooks us sausages and chips, and sits down with us. She has a smoke and a sherry and says, Playing out after tea, Hughie?

She says, You're as well being out with your pals on a nice night like this.

Then I want to tell her something. But Linda's sitting there with a sausage pronged on her fork, waiting to get me back for making her get on the bus herself. So I just go out.

Now I've been running my skin is burning from the inside. I feel like my feet will send sparks running through the gravel in front of the house. I take my shirt off and hang it over the BED AND BREAKFAST sign. The arms hang down, pointing towards the ground. This is good. I go inside and find some things. An old coat, a scarf, a leaky pair of boots. Linda follows me out to see what I'm doing, and then together we make him. Once the coat's buttoned (which is difficult, getting the two sides together) you wouldn't think a big signpost was there at all. It's a MONSTER, Linda says. And because it's getting darker it does look good, if you step back a bit. Close up it's kind of squint and baggy. I say, he looks drunk, though. He looks like a SCARECROW, Linda says. No, I say, He looks like DAD, when he's pissed. Linda giggles, and I grab her shoulder and say, Let's leave him so when dad comes back and it's dark he'll think he'll think it's HIM...

Linda swivels round, she's hopeless, trying to cross her legs standing up so she won't pee. I push her down on the grass and tickle her to make it worse. She's laughing and screaming at me to stop but I won't, my fingers scrabbling in every direction like a nest of frantic spiders while she wriggles and squeals beneath me, Hughie STOP IT, HUGHIE, her arms are flying everywhere and I see the way to armpits where she'll really...

FUCK she's wet beneath me, sudden still. I skittle backwards till my leg goes blank where she's kicked me, very quick and hard, with her clumpy school shoes on. Then the hurt starts and spills everywhere, quivering through me to my fists, jarring till I hit her once, twice and then it's gone. She's on her feet, running for the house, and she shouts You're a big SHITE and the MONSTER'S SHITE as well.

I sit on the cool damp grass and rub my shin. Tomorrow a good ripe burst of purple there to show. It's nearly dark now, sitting in my t-shirt my arms begin to prickle as the night shivers down, but I won't take him to bits to get my shirt. I won't.

The new girl knows better already so it's her pal Janet

that said, Does the story have to be about something Missus Magregor?

Well yes Janet every story has to be ABOUT something, doesn't it?

But this time... this time you're going to write about
THE COUNTRYSIDE
She looks around the table, and her mouth gets smaller a bit, but maybe that's cause she's moved back. Hands in the air –

My GUEDNESS you would think none of you had ever heard of it before, and it's ALL AROUND US!

In the morning a car stops. They seen the sign. Kirsty takes them quickly inside. They don't see round the back where the rust piles sit in case it itches them off before they get their arses up the stairs. Round the back I sit, banging at a car door with a spanner, hear the heavy clung and see the rust flake and drift. But Kirsty's out with a blowtorch up her bum DON'T BE A BLOODY NEWSANCE and that. I'm away, I don't frigging care. There's places to be. Cut up the back over the spindly fence. There's no signs to tell the way, no Toadstool Trail, it just breathes me in. The sun turns down as I break into the trees, I have to throw my head right back to see where it creeps in, forty feet up. My feet go padding quiet on the dark bed, where the needles fall and lose their spiky tip, turn soft and damp and hush me in. Soon there's no sound except me breathing, that's no louder than a fern grows, than a nettle stings. Sometimes I just stand between two good strong trunks, waiting for their lowest branches to droop down and pull my fingers to the cool brown bark. My hair BLACK AS BUGGERY wouldn't dry and split on the forest's face, would grow down straight and smooth, fall in the needles' time. But now we need movement, like a bird breaking from the upper branches I know which way to go. With the forest fringe in sight, where the big field keeps guard in the sunshine, I silf through the trees, past the fallen king whose moulding broken back I have to climb, past the stinky burn, past the coiled silver snake of barbed wire some bastard left to mind me here I'm still not...

Then I hear them, sooner that I thought. Not right up to the Gartloan houses, so there playing in the woods, the wee boys? I have to go carefully now, my feet are furred and sure. I get down, moving my head slow, and see them, the Gordon boys, and her, the new girl. Nicholas Gordon is pointing upwards, and the others look where he shows them. His brother Simon says THAT'S NOTHING I'VE SEEN A MUCH BIGGER ONE then Nicholas and the girl are giggling. Simon shouts SHUT UP NICKLY AT LEAST I'VE and it goes on. But I wait until I'm aching, curled down as tight as the wire, and I wait after that, even though I'd like to spring, to catch that Simon Gordon on my barbs and watch him tug. And I don't know why I'm waiting except that they can't see me, their eyes can't tell me from the skin and bones of the forest that they play in like a paddling pool. And maybe I gather and grow and soar, hang fifty feet high, see them shrink when

THEY SEE ME READY TO CRASH
        and hearing my name, hearing her say my name, and
                you shouldny laugh at him and his sister it's not
come crashing down.

Dad's back. You can tell it's hot because he's taken his shirt off. Where I stand at the edge of the trees I can see what hairy shoulders he's got. Maybe the shirt burst off him, ape man, wolf man, goat. He's standing in the middle of the rustpile, scratching. He's got something new for the pile today, a big black pipe, it stretches up above the car it leans against. Maybe he's going to put both together and make a submarine. I think about him putting goggles on and waving goodbye before he steps inside it and drives down into the water.

I want to go inside, but I can't go straight in, on gravel even my feet crunch. So along the bank in the long grass, stepping CAREFUL a nettle (but nettles are nothing really, I once did a whole arm with them for a test, till I felt like army ants with spiky boots were running all over it, I just had to bite my lip) – and over the wall into the big field. My old man the silly bastard doesn't even turn round, when I check he's still staring away from me. So I go across the field and in by the front. See coming in from the sunshine it's so dark in the house it's like going into a different world. Something

NOW WHY IS IT WE READ STORIES,
AND SOMETIMES WRITE OUR OWN?

WELL? ANYBODY?

Kirsty's watching telly, except that she's not, she's asleep. She's got her mouth open. Old film on the telly, black and white. Man with a long coat and hat, then a woman singing in a room full of men. She's wearing a dress and these long white gloves, even though it's inside, and then she's taking them off, the gloves. Can I change the channel? Soon as I switch there's Kirsty's voice, Have you not got any homework to do? No.

Well, away out and play or something, it's a nice day.

So I go out again.

The new girl says, It's so we can go into different worlds.

I reckon I'll go to Lemahamish. I don't go down the road and through the campsite, I go by the woods. It's a way only I know. I used to be scared a bit, but not now. Someone told me stories. I think it was when I used to go to my gran's, or maybe in infants school, with the young teacher who left. Like real kid's stuff, like if you go into the woods alone you find a place that's magic, which is maybe always winter, or animals that can talk. All that kind of shite, except there was this one bit I really remember, about this hill near Aberdour. It's a real hill in the forest park, not high, all covered with trees. She said there was a story that if you walked round the hill anti-clock-wise seven times, you would disappear. Everyone believed it except this one man who said it wasn't true, and he would show it wasn't. So one day he goes out alone, he's told them where he's going. He does the seven times round, and he dis-appears. Everyone's out looking when he doesn't come back, but they don't find him, no body nor nothing. He's just gone. I kept thinking, where? Was he just dead, or did he go some-where else, another world? Or maybe he just dissolved, like they say VANISHED INTO THIN AIR, so that he was still there, carried about on the wind, and he could see the people looking for him, and maybe he wanted to say, Look, you were right, tell them it's true, but he couldn't tell them. He couldn't speak at all.

But that was ages ago I used to think about that, I know now that none of it's real.

It's lucky I go by the woods because I come out on the far bank, above the mudslide. Everybody is over the other side on the grass, all the campsite people with the radios and rugs. They all know the place because the warden put up signs

LEMAHAMISH POOL and SWIM AT YOUR OWN RISK.
Further up the river doesn't know about any of it, but it can't
go any other way. Winter is its favourite, it's high and fast
then, rushing noise with only me to hear, and the water
whirling down all raw. But even in summer it's good and the
pool is wide and deep between me and the other bank. Over
there it's old men with their foldy white bellies spilling out
onto the grass, and wee girls in knickers and shiny red wellies.
Big boys playing football and jumping over everybody, and the
kids from school. I'm just about to go away but it's too late
anyway, they've already HUEY already seen me. I don't look
up. I go down the mudslide, don't slip. There's this funny tree
growing straight out of the bank like a gangplank above the
water, I climb onto it and sit down. Then I work my way
along, watching my ripply reflection follow me. HUE-EE!
They're hopping over the stones to the water's edge OW MA
BLUDDY FOOT a big team of them WATERS FREEZING,
nearly the whole class, jumping about and shouting in front of
the campers. Drew and Tommy are into the river first, grab-
bing and shrieking as the water fills their shorts. The new girl
is next. She's in a black swimming costume and her arms and
legs are brown, like she's been on holiday abroad. She swades
into the water with long steps, until her legs disappear. She
stands still, looking at the water lapping at her waist. Palming
the surface with her hands, her face goes tight with frowning
for a minute, then she plunges. She's up again in a gasp, pushing weeds of hair off her face, then she swims after Tommy
and Drew. She soon catches up with them, her arms come out
of the black water like knives, out in the middle where it's
deep. She turns over easily to shout COME ON at the others
still shivering thigh-deep, Janet and big Graham and Simon
Gordon. Then Janet scoops her hand through the water and
splashes Simon, the skinny wank, and Graham jumps backwards, catching Janet in his tidal wave and suddenly they're
all in the water kicking and waving arms and legs, turning
everything to froth. HEY CAN YOU DIVE WATCH THIS
and Janet's telling Graham he canny dive so AM GONNY
DROWN YOU JANET MACKIE and the black pool under
the fir trees is sliced open with Janet screaming. Watching it,
Drew says something to Tommy, and then launches towards
the new girl, arms beating through the water like a swimming
windmill. And she doesny even move, she just treads water,

reaches out at the last second to hold him off. It's the same in the playground, she won't run even when they both go for her, mouths open, hands low for her legs. She never ran away from boys in the CITY. Now in the river Drew grabs at her beneath the water. Next second his face goes surprised and she's threshing away from him, towards my bank. This time she's getting (Fucking dae that tae me ye wee cunt!) getting out of it, climbing out of the water, past me, up the mudslide. She doesn't look at me, just sits down on the grass at the top of the bank, stretching her legs for the sun to warm, and shivering a bit. And the rest of them follow her. I think, shouldn't she be at home writing her wee story, I think but this is nae use, I see Drew's face sneery with hating her, and I'm half hoping he'll do something. I hope that HUE-EE I hope but Graham's already lifting his dripping black head toward me. He sways a bit, grinning at me. I could kick him in the face. I could kick him hard in the mouth where HUEY! his lips could burst and bleed. WHAT YE DOING HERE, HUEY! Graham on one side, rearing out of the water. Tommy and Drew forgetting about the girl on the other, they came across the mudbank towards me, with Simon Gordon trailing smirking behind. I watch where their wet feet churn the mud till it squelches. What ye doing HERE, Huey? Simon Gordon says, It's too HOT the junkyard's getting SMELLY. Like people cross themselves him and Janet pinch their noses shut. Tommy disappears from my sight, I'm staring straight ahead down the river, where it heads for the north sea.

It's no a JUNKYARD says Drew, it's a HOTEL it's HUEY's Hotel isn't Hue? Graham laughs, he says its Huey's Smelly Hotelly.

I know that Tommy's behind me, I can feel his weight press down on the trunk. Someone says You shouldny be sitting there Huey ye canny SWIM.

This is how it happens. I'm lying on the bank. I'm wet, I'm cold even though the sun is soaking the rest of Lemahamish in the afternoon sleeps, mud in my mouth. The rest of them are back in the water, shouting insults at the tourists. Except for the new girl, she's standing a few feet away. She looks like she doesn't know what to do. But she won't have to wait long. See the tree I was sitting on? That's what they can all see. But they don't know what goes on underneath, all the hoops and loops

and tendrils, the strong wet stretch of green skin. Simon goes
first, without time to shout. Janet manages one good scream
before her mouth fills, and then there's big Graham gaping IT
WISNY ME before he goes too, pudgy hands clamouring in
the air for a bit after his head's disappeared. Drew screams
HELP ME but by the time the big campsite boys get into the
water there's no sign of him. One of the boys dives after him. I
wonder what he'll see down there through the grey seep, faces
white and cold already, weeded hands and feet pulling the eel-
meat slowly home? He doesn't come up again. His pal reaches
Tommy where he struggles and tugs at thin air, but just as he
gets hold of him, his own face twists with alarm. The both of
them going down together.

Nobody else follows, the campsite mob all prancing and
dancing on the far bank, the smartest ones already pushing
onto the narrow track that winds back to the sites. Soon the
place is cleared, the stood-on radios dead. The bright stripy
rugs they've left behind them, like giant sweetie-wrappers on
the quiet grass. I'm picking myself up from where I've been
lying, still as a log and nearly the right colour, when I hear this
noise behind me. I'd forgotten about her. She seen everything
they done. Rather than risk the swim she's headed for the
forest, running, on her bare feet. I wonder if she'll make it
home OK.

John Maley

THE WILD COLONIAL BOY

England's got its teeth in my tongue,
as rough as cardboard on the young.
History like a hard lesson, some old
schoolmaster with soup on his tie,
smelling of sawdust, whisky and sick,
forgets the good and great we done.
Poverty is a slow violence, it hovers
at your heart like a cocked gun.
Poverty is exile of a kind, mapping
the hungriest years of a native son.
I'm a wild colonial boy on a giro,
the apprentice sent for tartan paint.
I wish for word of rude rebellion.
I dream of treason in the kingdom.

BENTSHOT

A black sheep with woolly notions
that love lurks in the locality.
Grew up, the world growled up,
thinking it was the worst thing.
I've blown through blind dates,
bruised lives and burnt trust.
I was 22 before I could say
this thing out loud. But I
shouldn't wear a kind of love
like a shroud. I shouldn't fear
my own life, unwise, unwieldy.
After all, I'm brave, I've given.
To you, the man whose hatred
of love I've driven like a stake
into my heart. Hurting, since
then I've swallowed my pride
and an oil-rig worker's cock.
But bitter with blame, all
I could taste was your name.

Gordon Meade

CATFISH

Almost uglier than a monk,
A catfish, with a massive head
And flapping tail, unable to be
Contained within the framework
Of a wooden crate. Garnished

With light, its rough-grained
Skin, a lunar blue, glows above
Handfuls of manufactured ice.
Warily, a young boy pokes his
Fist into the dog-toothed mouth.

Myopic eyes stare back at his
Unnecessary doubts. In the oily
Stench of the harbour a family cat
Has drowned. It floats face-down
Amongst discarded rubber gloves

And crushed tin-cans. Peering
Into cloudy water, all its pickled
Eyes can see, is the same as the
Catfish saw on the cluttered quay –
Death's five-fingered hand –

The invisible grip of the sea.

Màiri NicGumaraid

DAN DO LEODHAS

B' fhada b' fhada mo mhiann
Fuireach gun falbh
Is dh'fheuch mi cho fada 's a b' urrainn dhomh
Uair tilleadh gun mhaill
Cha b' e an diugh
Cha b' e an dè
No uair a tha rè
An ama-sa

Is uair
Is uair eile

Is b' fheudar dhomh falbh
Is falbh
Is falbh
'S mo chianalas chrochadh nam dhèidh

Is b' fheudar dhomh falbh
Is falbh
Is fuireach air falbh
'S mo chianalas chrochadh nam dhèidh

Cha d' fhuair mi cothrom a thoirt leam
Bha e ro throm
'S bha a' ghàire aotrom
Aighearach

Is i a dh'fhill mi ri Glaschu
Far am buin mi nis
An dràsda
A nis
An dràsda co-dhiù

Ach bha mi òg an Leòdhas
Is bidh mi òg an Leòdhas gu bràth

Mary Montgomery

POEM FOR LEWIS

Long long was my desire
To remain
And I tried as long as I could
Once returning without delay
Not today
Not yesterday
Or a time during
This time

And a time
And another time

And I had to go
And go
And go
And hang my homesickness behind me

And I had to go away
And go
And stay away
And hang my homesickness behind me

I didn't get a chance to take it with me
It was too heavy
And the laughter was light
And joyful

It was what plied me to Glasgow
Where I now belong
At present
Now
At present anyway

But I was young in Lewis
And I'll be young in Lewis forever

Edwin Morgan

FOR SORLEY MacLEAN'S 80th BIRTHDAY

Out of the west came a thick mist,
It hid the gabbro and the schist,
And got the Cuillin in a twist.
– I've seen worse, said Sorley.

A black storm battered the Quiraing,
Bolts from the blue sent down their bang,
Clapped-out sea-bells rolled and rang.
– Breeze getting up, thought Sorley.

Then Gabriel blew his dizzy trump,
Tombstones fell back with a thump,
Satan roared and scratched his rump.
– What's all that, asked Sorley.

Next day the sun jumped up like Punch,
And midges took an early lunch,
And poet's feet made shingle crunch.
– There you go, sang Sorley.

Gus Morrison

E.T. IN GLASGOW

I met a Martian in Reids O' Pertyck,
Sitting among the revolutionaries, weekend hippies;
loners with copies of Lenin in their jouks – the usual
Seventies Saturday night division –
kiddin on they didnae want a lumber.

He was drinking beer shandies and vodka 'n' lime,
frae a toty wee glass shaped like the European Cup.

The pub was noisy but he was quiet.
Feeling a bit oot o' things –
naebody paying him any heid – a wee bit of discrimination frae
the usual punters.
At least that's whit I thought
until I remembered that Martians don't bother wie a
blether (even when they've hud a few).
Naw, seemingly communication is done on a higher level;
telepathy – E.S.P. – thought transference.
Fax was still tae be invented.

I sat beside him cos I'm no a bigot
and we shared a few quiet thoughts
in amongst the Hullabaloo
before the bouncers turfed us onto Dumbarton Road.
The Martian for sleeping and me for shouting obscenities
aboot Rangers tae a wee hard man wie a Blue Nose.

Things huv changed and Martians are pretty common
along with other extra terrestrials
but in they days they were few and far between
and the pubs in the West End operated discriminatory
policies, especially in Byres Road.

Dòmhnall Rothach
Donald Munro

Bithidh an raon air thuileachadh le feur ùr
is an ràineach a' luasgadh
mar fheamainn anns an t-sùmainn.
Bithidh siùil gheala nan sgitheach
air an togail ris a' ghaoith,
agus lusan bheaga, bhuidhe is gheala,
a' dealrachadh
mar choinnle-Brianain anns a' ghuirme.

Slaodaidh a' ghrian reobhart
thar gàrradh liath na raoin;
am measg nan craobh crìon cnàmhach,
bolg reobhairt san aimsir mhàithreil;
reobhart gàirdeach feòir ùir.

The field will be flooded with fresh grass
and the bracken waving
like seaweed in the surge.
The white sails of the hawthorns
will be hoisted to the wind,
and little flowers, yellow and white,
glittering
like phosphorescence in the green.

The sun will drag a springtide
over the grey dykes of the field;
amongst the withered bony trees,
the swollen belly of springtide in the mothering season;
a joyful springtide of new grass.

Ailish Petrie

THE LITTLE TEDDY BEAR AND THE WITCH

A little teddy-bear was looking for his Mummy because his Mummy had left his Daddy. On the road she met a rabbit and beside the rabbit there were lots of carrots. She asked if she could have some carrots but the rabbit said NO! THESE ARE MINE THIS IS MY PROPERTY. So the little teddy-bear said PLEASE IT'S NOT FOR ME IT'S FOR MY MUMMY... COULD I HAVE JUST ONE CARROT?
YES O.K. said the rabbit.

Further up the road the little teddy-bear met a monkey who had a lot of bananas and he asked the monkey if he could have some bananas but the monkey said NO! These are mine. This is my property. So the little teddy-bear began to shout and scream and scream... until the monkey couldn't listen to it any more and so the monkey covered his ears and said O.K. TAKE THEM, TAKE THEM. And so the little teddy-bear put the bananas in a basket and went along the road until he met a worm with some cherries... and he asked the worm if he could have some cherries. YOU CAN HAVE THREE said the worm.
THREE ARE NOT ENOUGH said the little teddy-bear. And so the worm gave him ten and he put them into the basket.

Finally the little teddy-bear arrived at his house... but there was a witch outside and the witch said GIVE ME EVERYTHING, EVERYTHING NOW. But the little teddy-bear said no, these are mine. I found them. This is my property. And they began to fight and while they were fighting a mole came along and ran away with the basket... and they didn't see the mole because they were fighting. Then suddenly, at the same time they realised that the basket was missing.
YOU'VE GOT IT said the witch.
YOU'VE GOT IT said the little teddy-bear.
YOU'VE GOT IT... YOU'VE GOT IT... YOU'VE GOT IT... and then they both said WHERE IS MY DINNER? WHERE IS MY DINNER?

After a while the witch went off to the right and the little teddy-bear went off to the left.
The little teddy-bear finds a carrot.
The witch finds a banana.
The little teddy-bear finds a cherry.
The witch finds a cherry.
The little teddy-bear finds a cherry
The witch finds a cherry.
The little teddy-bear finds a cherry
The witch finds a cherry.
The little teddy-bear finds a cherry
The witch finds a cherry.
The little teddy-bear finds a cherry.
1, 2, 3, 4, 5, 6, 7, 8, 9 cherries so there is one cherry missing.

This time the witch goes off to the left and the little teddy-bear goes off to the right.

The little teddy-bear finds the mole and cuts the mole's belly open and inside he finds the last cherry... and then the little teddy-bear sews up the mole's belly and goes off to the fox's grotto.

The witch has found the fox and cuts open the fox's belly but inside there is nothing except the hand of a man.

The little teddy-bear collects up all the food and goes home to his mother.

The witch sews up the fox's belly and the fox eats the witch.

Richard Price

AT EASE
in memory of my mother

Scotland hits eighty in May.

An electric mower blows its nose.
The explaining murmur is my father by the ladders;
the MacMillan visitor, months into this conversation,
is at ease.

With my shirt off, everything is ridiculous:
dad in shorts and people in the wrong places.
Inside, like church, where mum says garden
she means an English one.

THE DAY BEFORE MY MOTHER'S FUNERAL

Tilt all your body in the lane's dash
and you're parallel with the rain.
The two brothers seem to know this:
ahead, they miss every drop.

We know our jackets again, heavy
as if someone else's, cloth wet through.
My hand in your hand
in your lined deep pocket.

Behind us my father holds his fishing
hat not tightly to his head and runs,
walks and runs.

Wayne Price

SALMON

The dog appeared just as the last of the voices faded away, a
black, hungry-looking lurcher. It stood still at the lip of the
high river bank, staring down across the cold quick water at
him. Then it twisted away and disappeared into the field
behind, maybe after the voices. He shrugged his pack up and
forward towards his shoulders and walked on. Suddenly the
dog reappeared, again on the edge of the high, undercut bank
opposite, now a little way ahead of him. This time it stayed
and watched him labour on under his pack and fishing tackle
until he had long passed it and was out of sight around the
wide sweep of the river bend.

He finally made the road bridge at noon and after climbing to it from the river bank was glad to rest there. The sun
was punishing on his bare neck and head and inside his boots
his hot feet were soft-feeling and soaked with sweat and blis-
ter-water. He rested his rod against the stone parapet of the
bridge, struggled out of his pack and creel and leaned back
alongside his rod, his arms splayed to support him. After a
while he stooped down and worked a plastic water bottle out
of a side pocket of his pack, drank from it and then poured
some of the water over his head. It felt warm, like the fluid in
his boots, and the smell of hot tarmac from the road mingled
queasily in his nose and throat with the plastic scent of the
water from the bottle. He twisted the top back on and re-
packed it.

Turning away from the road he leaned to look over the
parapet into the river. The better trout would all be aligned
just under the arch, out of sight, behind the shadow-line, but
he could see the occasional glint upstream of the younger,
smaller fish as they turned to take food under the rippled surface, then as they turned again to find their lies in the open
river, out in the full glare of the sun. He wished he'd had the
sense to stay near the bridge to fish, pitching the tent after
dark maybe, instead of walking so far upriver to the quieter
stretches. He supposed he would have had plenty of chances
under the bridge, even in this weather.

There was still another half-hour or so of walking before

reaching the town, he reckoned. He hoisted the rucksack up onto the lip of the parapet, tilting its weight from there onto his shoulders, then slipping his arms through its straps, moving forward and taking the strain. The fishing rod and creel he carried first in one hand, then the other, using the tip of the cotton rod-bag to flick the sweat away from his eyes.

As he walked through the main street the little town seemed deserted. For a while he didn't even see any traffic, then a loud, skinny-looking dirt-bike tore past him from behind, turned at the head of the street and passed him again, this time the boy riding it looking full into his face.

At the empty bus-stop he set down his fishing gear and slid off the pack. The long street, sweeping in a gentle curve down and away from him, seemed to channel a faint breeze and he turned his back to it, letting it cool the wetness between his shoulders. At last a few cars sped past, and a small white camper slowed and parked outside the post office some fifty yards or so down the street. A cafe was open just a few doors along from the bus-stop and leaving his gear he walked stiffly down to it.

The cafe was surprisingly cool inside. A girl in a dirty blue apron was wiping down a big steel tea-urn behind the counter.

Have you got any cold coke? he asked.

In the fridge, there.

He looked around for the fridge, finding it just behind his back, half hidden by the open door of the cafe. The girl finished cleaning the urn before serving him, then took the money in a hand still damp from the rag she'd been using.

Back outside the cafe he saw that a small, awkward-looking man was eyeing his gear. The fisherman watched him from the door of the cafe, drinking the coke in the shade, taking big, painful gulps that were hard to keep down. He drained the can quickly, then dropped it into a big bin at his side. He belched, and a little coke came back up, still cold.

As he approached the man looked up from the pack and tackle and nodded. The fisherman nodded back and stood over the rucksack, creel and rod.

Eh, Jesus, I'll be glad to get on home. Been working from four this morning, me. He grinned shyly at the fisherman.

Aye? said the fisherman. He felt another belch start to force itself. He eased it out.

It's all paid for, mind. He had a reedy voice and kept

nodding his head down to the side as he spoke. He had a
small, boyish face but the narrow chin and jaw lines were
peppered with a ginger stubble. The stubble didn't match his
thinning hair, which was watery brown, like his eyes. He kept
on grinning. Aye, he said again, and looked set to go on talking, but first he spooned a pat of soft ice-cream out from a
plastic tub and into his mouth. Aye, I'll be glad to get home
mind, he said after swallowing.

The fisherman nodded. Know when the bus's due, pal?

The man spooned in another lump of ice-cream, this time
talking through it. Couldn't say. Usually I get me a lift home
from the slaughterhouse like, but it's overtime season now.

Oh aye, the slaughterhouse? he said, interested.

Aye. A tear of ice-cream welled at the corner of his mouth
and started to trickle. He smeared it with the back of his hand.

What's it you do there then?

The man cleared his throat. I'm on the tripe bags, me.
Mind I can do the guts too.

The fisherman looked more closely at the crusty brown
specks he'd already noticed sprinkling the collar at the front
of the man's white T-shirt. Is it cows you do?

Aye, cows and lambs. And the odd pig, like. Mainly lambs
now mind, this time of year. Two thousand through today.
That's how I was in early like.

Lamb shit, thought the fisherman. And there were more
tiny stains he noticed now, some on the side of his chin and
one on his right ear lobe. Some of them were darker and
smoother. Blood, he decided. He looked down and saw his
boots were soiled too. They were big and steel-toe capped, but
apart from the specks they were yellow, like big, dangerous
clown's boots.

The man started scraping the last of the ice-cream with
the little plastic scoop, but it was too far gone in the heat. He
gave up and drank the remains straight from the tub.

The fisherman looked at his watch. He sighed. Christ, it's
hot, he said.

Aye, the slaughterhouse man said.

The fisherman tipped his pack and sat on it, levelling his
legs out onto the road. Must be a hell of a job, he said. I
worked in a bloody sausage factory once and Jesus, that was
bad enough.

The slaughterhouse man blinked down at him, surprised.

Naw, he said mildly, and shook his head. Naw, it's fantastic, being with all the lads, like. He placed the empty ice-cream tub at his feet, next to the yellow boots, and then straightened back up. A great job. They're great lads, like. And I can get a whole lamb for the mother for thirty quid, me. Thirty quid! And I *know* it's been killed the day. Oh aye. Aye it's great. He fumbled in a pocket and found a pack of Embassy Milds. He offered one of the Milds to the fisherman, but he shook his head. The slaughterhouse man lit up and drew down hard, then breathed it back contentedly. Thirty or forty depending on size, like, he said.

Behind them the door of the hotel snapped shut and they both turned. A heavy, red-faced man strolled over to them. He stopped between them and looked from one to the other. In the end he spoke to the fisherman.

Still no fucking bus, eh? I've been watching from that window there since five o' fucking clock. Another bastard cock-up, eh? He stared down at the fisherman, then at the fishing tackle. He worked his top lip from the inside with his tongue and the thick brown clump of his moustache shrugged and bristled. His tongue found something and scooped it back and he took his time mashing it with his front teeth. Five past fucking five, eh?

The fisherman shook his head and stood up.

Been fishing, eh pal? He picked up the rod and felt for the sections inside the cotton bag. Is it for trout this is for then? He belched and the fisherman caught a stale waft of beer.

The fisherman nodded, watching the man's thick fingers stumbling over the slim tubes under the cloth.

Too fucking wee for salmon.

Well, aye.

The man snorted. Aye by Christ. He looked away across the road. Up in the hills? He tilted the rod to the wide gap between a garage and a church on the opposite side of the wide street. Through it the hills were visible, rolling back into the pale late afternoon haze. The fisherman nodded, and the big man turned to the slaughterhouse worker. You too, pal?

Naw. He grinned, embarrassed. I work in the slaughterhouse, me. Back there. He pointed.

Two young girls stepped out onto the road just where he was pointing. They looked at him and giggled, whispering something. A small white terrier was nosing around their legs, but they were oblivious to it. They hurried across to the three men, the dog following, then hurried on past and waited behind them, leaning whispering against the wall of the hotel the big man had come from. The big man tracked them with his eyes, then stared off into space. Finally he turned back to the man from the slaughterhouse.

Is it still the old gun you use there, then?

The slaughterhouse man blinked, uneasy at the tone of the question. Well, aye, for the cows, like, with the bolt, aye. But you've got your prongs mind, for the lambs.

The big man laid the rod back against the bus-stop and lifted two fingers to either side of his head, just behind the ears. Like that, he said. Right pal?

Aye! The slaughterhouse man brightened, seeming happy that the stranger knew something about his work. He edged closer to him. Hey, I tell you what though, the buckets came in the day and the first thing I had to say to the boss was naw, no good, send them back! Send them back? he says. Aye, I say. Too big! I say. Aye, they were too big for the little plastic chutes, too big to go under them like. He shook his head, grinning, then took another drag on his cigarette. There was quiet for a while.

That's my place there, the big man said, thumbing back at the hotel where the girls were leaning. Chef. Head Chef.

The other two men nodded.

Hey pal, it's you we get our steaks from I reckon, he said to the slaughterhouse man.

Well, I wouldn't know that like, but aye mebbe.

Aye. You kill the bastards all wrong, mind.

The slaughterhouse man looked up at him, blinking again.

Right enough you do, pal. That bolt thing, it's a bastard for bruising. Ruins the off-cuts every shot, and your good cuts too, now and again. The bruising spreads like fuck, see. Toughens the meat.

The fisherman watched the chef's face, wondering. It sounded like bullshit, but there wasn't any smile. The slaughterhouse man twisted his face doubtfully.

Listen pal, said the chef, what colour is a lobster when you catch it, eh?

It's ... aye it's red, like.

No, no pal, when it's fucking *caught*.

The slaughterhouse man fidgeted with his cigarette, widened

his stance. Aye, well brown like.

No, no it's fucking *blue*, eh? It goes *red* because the hot water you drop it into touches its brain, and that makes it bruise, pal. It's a *bruise*, all that red, all over the fucker. Whoosh. Now see what I mean about the bolt and your cow and that, eh? It's all in the *brain*, pal. He tapped his skull and smiled.

Aye, mebbe like. He shrugged and went back to his cigarette. The dog that had crossed the road behind the girls suddenly appeared at his feet, sniffing around his legs and spattered boots. For a while it got distracted by the empty ice-cream tub, but soon went back to the boots. He watched the dog for a while, then caught the fisherman's eye. Hey, it's all that tripe he's smelling, eh? On the boots like. They both looked back down at the dog. It started to lick at one of the ankles and the man let it, then it took hold of a lace and looked like using its teeth and the slaughterhouse man nudged it away with a yellow steel toe-cap. It tried again and got another, sharper dig in the ribs, then lay down in the sun near the boots and yawned.

The fisherman saw the girl from the cafe come out without her apron carrying a long wooden pole. She used it to push back the awning over the window, went back inside with it and reappeared moments later with a stooping man who locked the door behind them. They both got into his car which pulled off sharply, U-turned across the road and accelerated up the street towards the bus stop. She looked straight ahead as they passed.

The two young girls suddenly appeared at his side, brushing between him and the chef. They made a show of looking up and down the empty road, then rushed across, the leading girl snorting with held laughter. Both men watched them trot over into the garage forecourt and on into its refreshments shop.

Those two crazy bitches came in on the bus with me this morning, the chef said in a low voice. Fucking giggling like that all the way. Aye by Christ. He turned to the slaughter-house man, pushing with his tongue behind both lips before speaking. Anyway pal, I don't go much for steak anyway, he said.

Eh, I love a bit of steak, me, the slaughterhouse man replied, interested again. It's great, steak is.

Nah. You know what I like? I like to get a bit of garlic, see? Tomatoes, chopped onions, those fucking courgettes, right? And a few mushrooms, and cover the lot with fucking brandy, after you've made a ring of sliced potatoes first mind, fried nice and covered in cheese, plenty of herbs like, and set fire to the brandy and serve it up like that, with all the flames still going. Fucking tasty, that is.

Aye, said the slaughterhouse man.

Bugger to eat mind, said the fisherman.

The chef worked the underside of his lips again before answering. Aye, all those flames, he said. That's right.

The street was busier now, traffic getting back from the city, the fisherman guessed. The heavy air was starting to taste of dust and petrol. The chef had taken hold of the rod again and was fingering it through the cloth. The fisherman watched him, then looked over to the slaughterhouse man. He was staring away into space, and the fisherman couldn't tell if he was grinning or wincing into the low sun. The dog at his feet was alert now, flicking his head after traffic, sniffing the air. Out of the corner of his eye the fisherman saw the two girls stood at the edge of the garage forecourt, waiting arm in arm for a break in the traffic. He turned to watch them and they leaned forward off the kerb and onto the road. He felt the chef at his side and realised he was tilting the rod in the girls' direction, pointing them out. I tell you what, son, he said in a low, restful voice, if I was fourteen I'd have those two up in those hills alright, the pair of them, up in the bushes up there. That's what they want when they're fucking fourteen by Christ, up in the bushes like that, they can't help it, I'm telling you, straight up son, straight fucking up.

The fisherman looked along the angle of the rod to the girls, still hesitating, just off the kerb; then up to the hills in the distance at their backs. There were no bushes, only the bare folds of the slopes, and out beyond the slopes a smoky, hot haze, up above them an empty evening sky, and somewhere amongst them a cold, quick river.

Alison Reid

BUMBLING

It was a bumbling day, black nuns in cool dresses, blowing in the tresses of the breeze. They brought Gran home, she who had been for so long my mother. Down the garden path, led by two shaking nurses, musing over a dandelion drink.

They said I shouldn't have left her out in the rain. I smiled a sly smile, and turning on my heel rebuked them. I went into the peppermint darkness smartly. Brandishing a glass of lemonade I re-emerged a fuller person. Without giving away the smallest particle of myself I talked to them all day. My mouth was an open cavern in my face. Two small tonsils moving up and down, vibrating like a feather in an Indian's bow.

There were dreams at each and every window of my house. I hid in the attic like a child. Remembered something every once and a while. I waved an endearing chuckle to the neighbours. A blackbird swivelled on the high wire of the telephone line. Summer was here again.

Days later I saw that they were still there, the nurses sitting on striped deckchairs on the lawn. They were sucking their thumbs. Gran was white haired and smiling. She poured the tea. She used our best china, and the tall silver teapot from Istanbul. The liquid gasped as it dived into the cups. You could see the sun through the bone. Shining. I could see into Gran's head.

Under the grass I could see worms moving. Translucent worms that wriggled. I laughed. The whole world was alive and wriggling. I could see everything. The red blood that pulsed in their skin. The ticking of the pupils in their eyes. I could see thoughts turning over in their heads, dark inky things. Ha... Ha... Ha... someone was planning seduction.

I thought it was best to iron out my life. I took the iron from the cupboard and set to. The fridge was open. Some food hopped on to the plates. Sandwiches at the ready. Lunch preparing. I picked up a pillow slip and pressed. Sleep slipped out newly laundered. Ready for bed.

I wasn't ready yet. And besides there was much still to be ironed out. Where was Jeremy for a start? Down by the river I expect. Lazy days stripped to the waist. Just like a Man down

by the river. And there was Gran having to take out lunch.
Having to entertain the guests. So white in their starched
linen.

At what time would the seduction emerge? When would it
begin? When Mrs Jones emerged from the shed. Giant jars of
pickled things. Mrs Jones fat around the bones. Mrs Jones.
When will your husband come home? Or Mr Black thin in his
driving car. Mr Black is it you who will seduce us?

Seduce us. Oh no, we're much too clever to be seduced.
And Gran still smiling, conversation spilling down her blouse.
Her big hands making pictures. Talking on. Unaware of the
dark stains under the lawn. Unaware of the seduction.

Dilys Rose

ALL THE LITTLE LOVED ONES

I love my kids. My husband too, though sometimes he asks me whether I do, asks the question, Do you still love me? He asks it while I am in the middle of rinsing spinach or loading washing into the machine, or chasing a trail of toys across the kitchen floor. When he asks the question at a time like that it's like he's speaking an ancient, forgotten language. I can remember a few isolated words but can't connect them, can't get the gist, don't know how to answer. Of course I could say, Yes I love you, still love you, of course I still love you. If I didn't still love you I wouldn't be here, would I, wouldn't have hung around just to go through the motions of companionship and sex. Being alone never bothered me. It was something I chose. Before I chose you. But of course, that is not accurate. Once you become a parent there is no longer a simple equation.

We have three children. All our own. Blood of our blood, flesh of our flesh etc., delivered into our hands in the usual way, a slithering mess of blood and slime and wonder, another tiny miracle.

In reply to his question my husband really doesn't want to hear any of my irritating justifications for sticking around, my caustic logic. He doesn't really want to hear anything at all. The response he wants is a visual and tactile one. He wants me to drop the spinach, the laundry, the toys, sweep my hair out of my eyes, turn round, away from what I'm doing and look at him, look lovingly into his dark, demanding eyes, walk across the kitchen floor – which needs to be swept again – stand over him as he sits at the table fingering a daffodil, still bright in its fluted centre but crisp and brown at the edges, as if it's been singed. My husband wants me to cuddle up close.

Sometimes I can do it, the right thing, what's needed. Other times, when I hear those words it's like I've been turned to marble or ice, to something cold and hard and unyielding. I can't even turn my head away from the sink, far less walk those few steps across the floor. I can't even think about it. And when he asks, What are you thinking? Again I'm stuck. Does it count as thinking to be considering whether there is time to bring down the laundry from the pulley to make room for the next load before I shake off the rinsing water, pat the leaves dry, chop off the stalks and spin the green stuff around the magimix? That's usually what my mind is doing, that is its activity and if it can be called thinking, then that's what I'm doing. Thinking about something not worth relating.

What are you thinking?

Nothing. I'm not thinking about anything.

Which isn't the same thing. Thinking about nothing means mental activity, a focusing of the mind on the fact or idea of nothing and that's not what I am doing. I've no interest in that kind of activity, no time for it, no time to ponder the true meaning of life, the essential nature of the universe and so on. Such speculation is beyond me. Usually when I'm asked what I'm thinking my mind is simply vacant and so my reply is made with a clear, vacant conscience.

I'm approaching a precipice. Each day I'm drawn nearer to the edge. I look only at the view. I avoid looking at the drop but I know what's there. At least, I can imagine it. I don't want to be asked either question, the conversation must be kept moving, hopping across the surface of our lives like a smooth flat stone.

... Thought is not the point. I am feeling it, the flush, the rush of blood, the sensation of, yes, swooning. It comes in waves. Does it show? I'm sure it must show on my face the way pain might, the way pain would show on my husband's face...

Do you still love me? What are you thinking?

Tonight I couldn't even manage my usual, Nothing. It wouldn't come out right, I try it out in my head, practise it, imagine the word as it would come out. It would sound unnatural, false, a strangled, evasive mumble or else a spat denial. Either way it wouldn't pass. It would lead to probing. A strained, suspicious little duet would begin in the midst of preparing the dinner and I know where this edgy, halting tune leads, I know the notes by heart.

(Practice makes perfect. Up and down the same old scales until you can do them without tripping up, without twisting fingers or breaking resolutions, without swearing, yelling, failing or resentment at the necessity of repetition. Without scales the fingers are insufficiently developed to be capable of... until you can do it in your sleep, until you *do* do it in your sleep, up and down as fast as dexterity permits. Without practice, life skills also atrophy.)

For years we've shared everything we had to share, which wasn't much at first and now is way too much. In the way of possessions at least. We started simply: one room, a bed we nailed together from pine planks and lasted a decade; a few lingering relics from previous couplings (and still I long to ditch that nasty little bronze figurine made by the woman before me. A troll face, with gouged-out eyes. Scary at night, glowering from a corner of the bedroom). Money was scarce but new love has no need of money. Somewhere to go, to be together is all and we were lucky. We had that. Hell is love with no place to go.

While around us couples were splitting at the seams, we remained intact. In the midst of break-ups and breakouts, we tootled on, sympathetic listeners, providers of impromptu pasta, a pull-out bed for the night, the occasional alibi. We listened to the personal disasters of our friends but wondered, in private, in bed, alone together at the end of another too-late night, what all the fuss was about. Beyond our ken, all that heartbreak, all that angst. What did it have to do with us, our lives, our kids? We had no room for it. Nor, for that matter, a great deal of space for passion.

An example to us all, we've been told, You two are an example to us all. Of course it was meant to be taken with a pinch of salt, a knowing smile but said frequently enough for the phrase to stick, as if our friends in their cracked, snapped, torn-to-shreds state, our friends who had just said goodbye to someone they loved, or someone they didn't love after all or any more, as if all of them were suddenly united in a wilderness of unrequited love. While we, in our dusty, cluttered home, had achieved something other than an accumulation of consecutive time together.

This is true, of course, and we can be relied upon to provide some display of the example that we are. My husband is likely to take advantage of the opportunity and engage in a bit of public necking. Me, I sling mud, with affection. Either way, between us we manage to steer the chat away from our domestic compatibility, top up our friends' drinks, turn up the volume on the stereo, stir up a bit of jollity until it's time to say Goodnight. See you soon. Look after yourself, until it's time to be left alone together again with our example. Our differences remain.

Do you still love me? What are you thinking?

Saturday night. The children are asleep. Three little dark heads are thrown back on pillows printed with characters from Lewis Carroll, Disney and Masters of the Universe. Three little mouths blow snores into the intimate, bedroom air. Upstairs, the neighbours hammer tacks into a carpet, their dogs romp and bark, their antique plumbing gurgles down the wall but the children sleep on, their sweet breath rising and falling in unison.

We are able to eat in peace, take time to taste the food which my husband has gone to impressive lengths to prepare. The dinner turns out to be an unqualified success: the curry is smooth, spicy, aromatic, the rice dry, each grain distinct, each firm little ellipse brushing against the tongue. The dinner is a joy and a relief. My husband is touchy about his cooking and requires almost as much in the way of reassurance and compliments in this as he does about whether I still love him or not. A bad meal dampens the spirits, is distressing both to the cook and the cooked-for. A bad meal can be passed over, unmentioned but not ignored. The stomach too has longings for more than simply to be filled. A bad meal can be worse than no meal at all.

But it was an extremely good meal and I was whole-hearted and voluble in my appreciation. Everything was going well. We drank more wine, turned off the overhead light, lit a candle, fetched the cassette recorder from the kids' room and put on some old favourites; smoochy, lyrical, emotive stuff, tunes we knew so well we didn't have to listen, just let them fill the gaps in our conversation. So far so good.

Saturdays have to be good. It's pretty much all we have. Of us, the two of us just. One night a week, tiptoeing through the hall so as not to disturb the kids, lingering in the kitchen because it's further away from their bedroom than the living room, we can speak more freely, don't need to keep the talk turned down to a whisper. We drink wine and catch up. It is necessary to catch up, to keep track of each other.

Across the country, while all the little loved ones are asleep, wives and husbands, single parents and surrogates are sitting down together or alone, working out what has to be done. There are always things to be done, to make tomorrow pass smoothly, to make tomorrow work. I look through the glasses and bottles and the shivering candle flame at my husband. The sleeves of his favourite shirt – washed-out blue with pearly buttons, last year's Christmas present from me – are rolled up. His elbows rest on the table which he recently sanded and polished by hand. It took forever. We camped out in the living room while coat after coat of asphyxiating varnish was applied. It looks good now, better than before. But was the effort worth the effect?

My husband's fine pale fingers are pushed deep into his hair. I look past him out of the kitchen window, up the dark sloping street at parked cars and sodium lights, lit windows and smoking chimneys, the blinking red eye of a plane crossing a small trough of blue-black sky. My house is where my life happens. In it there is love, work, a roof, a floor, solidity, houseplants, toys, pots and pans, achievements and failures, inspirations and mistakes, recipes and instruction booklets, guarantees and spare parts, plans, dreams, memories. And there is no need, nothing here pushing me. It is nobody's fault.

I go to playparks a lot, for air, for less mess in the house and of course because the kids like to get out. Pushing a swing, watching a little one arcing away and rushing back to your hands, it's natural to talk to another parent. It passes the time. You don't get so bored pushing, the little one is kept lulled and amenable. There's no way of reckoning up fault or blame or responsibility, nothing is stable enough, specific enough to be held to account and that's not the point. The swing swung back, I tossed my hair out of my eyes and glanced up at a complete stranger, a father. The father smiled back.

We know each other's names, the names of children and spouses. That's about all. We ask few questions. No need for questions. We meet and push our children on swings and sometimes we stand just close enough for our shoulders to touch, just close enough to feel that fluttering hollowness, like hunger. We visit the park – even in the rain, to watch the wind shaking the trees and tossing cherry blossoms on to the grass, the joggers and dog walkers lapping the flat green park – to be near each other.

Millions have stood on this very same ledge, in the privacy of their own homes, the unweeded gardens of their minds. Millions have stood on the edge and tested their balance, their common sense, strength of will, they have reckoned up the cost, in mess and misery, have wondered whether below the netless drop a large tree with spread branches awaits to cushion their fall. So simple, so easy. All I have to do is rock on my heels, rock just a shade too far and we will all fall down. Two husbands, two wives and all the little loved ones.

James Sherry

LINCHPIN

The hypodermic sun stimulates an optic
as the man with the bright blue moustache
smiles dark blue cheese. A fingerless
root taps its foot in endless invention
as skin becomes noticeably unreliable.
A disconsolate hat packs its bags and
heads for sunnier climes. Insects prefer
secondhand halos to first class returns.
The Big Top hits town with abbreviated
sadness. A clarinetist slits his wrists
when he discovers his wife in bed with
another trombone. An undertaker develops
an interesting sideline in homeopathic
lampshades while an albino tourist on
ice-skates demonstrates a unique method
of circumcision. Tropical fruit over-
throws a government, installs gas central
heating. Lugubrious policemen inhale
Venezuelan string quartets. An archbishop
undoes his flies, reveals surprised
asparagus. Unhinged, the linchpin loses
electrons. These lentils got wings.

Iain Crichton Smith

THE BRIDGE

My wife and I met them in Israel. They were considerably younger than us and newly married. They came from Devon and they had a farm which they often talked about. For some reason they took a fancy to us, and were with us a fair amount of the time, sometimes on coach trips, sometimes at dinner in the evenings. They were called Mark and Elaine.

I didn't like Israel as much as I had expected I would. I read the *Jerusalem Post* regularly, and was disturbed by some of the stories I found there, though the paper itself was liberal enough. There were accounts of the beatings of Palestinians, and pictures of Israeli soldiers who looked like Nazis.

Certainly it was interesting to see Bethlehem, Nazareth, the Garden of Gethsemane, and they reminded me of the security of my childhood: but at the same time seemed physically tatty, and without romance. Also we were often followed, especially in Jerusalem, by Arab school-children who tried to sell us postcards: the schools were in fact shut by official order.

Though this was the first time Mark and Elaine were abroad they were brighter than us with regard to money. Mark had a gift for finding out the best time for exchanging sterling and was, I thought, rather mean. Sometimes we had coffee in a foursome during the day or at night, and he would pull his purse out very carefully and count out the money: he never gave a tip. He was also very careful about buying for us exactly what we had bought for him on a previous occasion. On the other hand he bought his wife fairly expensive rings which she flourished expansively. They walked hand in hand. They were both tall and looked very handsome.

One day the coach took us to the Golan Heights. There were red flowers growing there, and some abandoned tanks were lying in a glade. The guide, who was a Jew originally from Iraq, told us that a few tanks had held off the attacks till the reservists had been called up. 'They can be called up very quickly,' he said. It was very peaceful, looking across the valley to the other side but there were notices about unexploded mines.

Often we met young boys and girls on the buses. They hitched rides from place to place in their olive green uniforms. They were of the age of schoolboys and schoolgirls. One morning on a bus I heard a girl listening to a pop song on a radio that she carried with her. It seemed very poignant and sad.

I used to talk quite a lot about articles I had read in the *Jerusalem Post*, which was my Bible because it was the only paper written in English. But neither Mark nor Elaine read much, not even the fat blockbusters that passengers on the coach sometimes carried with them. They told us a great deal about their farm, and what hard work it was. Then there was also a lot of paper work, including VAT. They were very fond of each other, and, as I have said, often walked hand in hand. He was very handsome: she was pretty enough in a healthy sort of way.

We were told by the guide a great deal about the history of Israel, about the Assyrians, about the Crusaders, about the Philistines. I especially remember a beautiful little simple Catholic church above Jerusalem. Then in Jerusalem we were shown the Via Dolorosa. At intervals along the route, young Jewish soldiers with guns were posted. 'Here is where Christ's hand rested,' said the guide, pointing to the wall. He himself had emigrated to Israel from Iraq. 'They took everything from us, even our clothes,' he said, 'for years we lived in a tent.' He had served in the paratroopers and was still liable for call-up.

We saw Masada, which was very impressive. Here the Jews had committed suicide *en masse* rather than surrender to the Romans. At one time the Israeli soldiers had been initiated into the army at a ceremony held at Masada, but that had been discontinued because of its passive associations. Thoughts of suicide were not useful against the Arabs.

I found it difficult to talk to the young couple about farming since I didn't know much about it. My wife, however, who had been brought up on a farm, chattered away about sheep, cattle, and hay. For myself I was more interested in the information I was getting from the *Jerusalem Post*. For instance, an American rabbi had said that the reason for the stone-throwing which had started was that the cinemas at Tel Aviv had been opened on a Saturday night.

We often saw Orthodox Jews wearing black hats, and beards. They sometimes read books while they were walking along the street. Also we saw many of them chanting at the Wailing Wall, where the men were separated from the women. My wife wrote a message and left it in the Wall as if it were a secret assignation. There was one comic touch: some of the Orthodox Jews covered their hats with polythene if it was raining, as the hats were very expensive.

I read diligently in the *Jerusalem Post*. Apparently in the past there has been stone-throwing against Jews. This was in mediaeval times and when they were living in Arab countries. But though Jews complained nothing was done about it. It was considered a reasonable sport.

My wife often used to wonder why Mark and Elaine had picked us for friends since they were so much younger. Did we look cosmopolitan, seasoned travellers, or did they simply like us? Sometimes Elaine talked to my wife as if she were talking to her mother. I found it hard to talk to Mark when the women were in the shops. He often spoke about money, I noticed, and was very exact with it. I sometimes thought that it was he who looked like the seasoned traveller, since he was always totally at ease and was excellent with maps.

The two of them didn't take so many coach trips as we did. Often they went away on their own, and we only met them in the evening.

They didn't go to the Holocaust Museum with us the day we went there. The place was very quiet apart from some French schoolchildren who scampered about. My wife hissed at them to be quiet, but they only grinned insolently. There were piles of children's shoes on the floor: these had been worn by victims of the Holocaust. There were many photographs, and a film that ran all the time.

There was also a room which was in complete darkness apart from thousands of candles reflected from a range of mirrors, so that it seemed that we were under a sky of stars. A voice repeated over and over again the names of the children who had been killed. The Jews had suffered terribly, but were now in turn inflicting terror themselves.

We met a woman who had come to Israel from South Africa. She opposed the Jewish attitude to the Palestinians, though she was a Jew herself. She said that mothers everywhere were against the continued war. She herself had driven her son in her own car to the front, not during the Seven Days war but the one after it.

We were in Israel on Independence Day. Jewish planes, streaming blue and white lines of smoke behind them, formed the Jewish flag. It was very impressive and colourful but also rather aggressive.

The coach took us to a kibbutz where we were to stay for two nights. Immediately we arrived, Mark and Elaine found that there were cattle there, and they left us in order to find out about the price of milk, etc.

The kibbutz itself had been raised out of a malarial swamp. Everyone had to work, and the place looked prosperous. It even had a beautiful theatre which the kibbutzers had built themselves. I ordered coffee from an oldish waiter, and when I offered him a tip he wouldn't accept it. I found out that he had been a lieutenant-colonel on Eisenhower's staff.

The kibbutzers, we were told by the guide, had their own problems. Sometimes when the young ones who had been reared in a kibbutz were called up on national service they entered an enviable world which they had not known of, and they left the kibbutz forever. Also some Jews had accepted compensation money from the Germans while others hadn't, and so there was financial inequality. Thus some could afford to take holidays while others couldn't. This introduced envy into the kibbutz.

Mark and Elaine were pleased with the cattle they had seen and full of praise. Mark had brought a notebook with him and had jotted down numbers of cattle, type of feeding stuff, etc. They had been given a tour of the farm with which they had been very happy.

One night they had told us that they recently had been in a place in England, it might have been Dorset, and they had come to a little bridge. There was a notice on the bridge that according to legend a couple who walked across the bridge hand in hand would be together forever. They smiled tenderly as they told us the story. In fact they had been on a coach trip at the time, and the passengers on the coach had clapped as the two of them volunteered to walk across the bridge. I thought it was a touching little story and I could imagine the scene; on the other hand I am not superstitious. 'How lovely,' said my wife.

My wife and I had been to Devon once. One day quite by accident we arrived at a house which was said to be haunted, and which had been turned into a restaurant. The owner of the restaurant, who made full use of the legend for commercial purposes, told us that many years before, there used to be criminals who used lanterns to direct ships onto the rocks. One man had done this only to find that one of the passengers on the wrecked ship had been his own daughter coming home from America. He had locked the body up in a room in his house. Many years afterwards the farmer who now owned the house noticed a mark on the wall which suggested the existence of an extra room. He knocked the wall down and found a skeleton there. An American tourist had said that she had seen the ghost of the young girl in broad daylight, and so had been born the legend of the Haunted House. So romance and death fed money and tourism.

We told Mark and Elaine the story, which they hadn't heard before. Suddenly there was a chill in the day as I imagined the father bending down to tear the jewellery from a woman's neck and finding that it was his own daughter.

'Should you like a coffee?' I said. I saw Mark fumbling with his purse. I thought of the Samaritan Inn which had been built at the presumed point where the Good Samaritan had helped his enemy. And indeed in Israel much of the biblical story had been converted into money.

Nevertheless I couldn't love Israel. There was too much evidence of Arab poverty. The dead bodies of Palestinian children were mixed up in my mind with the dead bodies of Jewish children. The mound of worn shoes climbed higher and higher.

On the last night of the tour we exchanged addresses. Mark and Elaine said they would write and my wife and I said we would do the same. And in fact we did do that for a while.

Today, this morning in fact, my wife received a letter from Elaine saying that she and Mark had split up. She said little, but reading between the lines we gathered that he had met a richer woman who was able to invest money in his farm.

We looked at each other for a long time, thinking of the young radiant couple who had walked hand in hand across the bridge.

Finally my wife said, 'At least they didn't have children. It would have been much worse if they had children.'

Valerie Thornton

NOVEMBER 91

I think I can see
your face
in my head
now.

But I know I can feel
your lips
on my eyes
and my brow
and my cheeks.

I cannot stop myself
from sucking my pen,
my finger tip,
the memory
of your lips
on mine.

In the darkening street
I cannot look them
in the eye,
these strangers
who would see desire
shining bright.

And in this dull twilight
I buy sunglasses
but I cannot keep my pinkie
from lodging
in the buttonhole
of my lapel.

SPRINGBOARD

With eau de Nil
rough as sandpaper
beneath your toes
you must wait
until your rings
of disturbed water
die against blue tiles.

This time
you must come
from a moment
however brief
of balance.

You must rise
to that weightless
turning point
and hang there
high above board
and pool
your heart still
and full for me

before the clean plunge
into deep water
as the board shudders
like sudden thunder.

Basil du Toit

THE INTERPRETATION OF DREAMS

Small ears grace your head, still tender,
without armouring hair. They hardly know
their work yet, just stuffing the pantry
with songnoises my voice is herding
towards them. Out of a darkness
I sing, like Rousseau's flautist
under a palm tree's green propeller.
But from what is happening right now
some of your dearest later joys may flow.

You will enter the forest, an amateur
explorer, your boots still factory-fragrant,
trying to trace strange honeys
to their source in wild, derelict hives.
But your expedition will bog down
in zones you have only heard about,
the realm of young parents in their prime,
living on in unreliable testament
and albums of red-pupilled photographs.

There you will stand, in spaceless black,
ready to give up and return.
But in the utter quiet your science
has brought you to, in the proximity
of alien orchids, uncollected insects,
uncharted families of arachnids,
just one more step might have taken you
out of that sheet of darkness
into this very room, this here and now

furnished by your mother from
auction sales and magazine coupons,
an evening room lit by common fixtures
where I am rocking you and singing to you
in my drab, drugging voice. This is
the simple place you can never reach,
though the trusting memory of your ears,
hoarding my song, is a storehouse
vaster than the granaries of Joseph.

Gael Turnbull

WILLIAM McTAGGART

On the sands of west Kintyre,
legs apart, slightly bent, facing
the surf, in a photograph, his son
holding the canvas against gusts
'first in my own rather than second
in any other' – no need to sign –
of which the best, he judged
were those few which had cost him
after much labour, the least

'never hurry, then, when everything
is as you chose, stop' – by power
to create space – the primer showing
as tinted ground with touches
of muted colour only in places
but those the right ones 'and
where harpies wait, though powerless
without aid, so do not lend yourself'
who held – to paint the wind.

Billy Watt

CONTRAFLOW

I

Carrying with us two spades
and one pickaxe, we started uphill
to follow the river's open vein.

The water coiled like liquid rust
among tenements, warehouses,
scooping shadows from long-forgotten

bridges. Then, spilling free from the cut
and thrust of city walls, it found
softer banks from which farm sumps

spurted yellow arteries. You
might not step in the same river twice
but you can franchise its groove and flow.

Sometimes as we climbed it faded
to a distant sibilance,
a tracery in partitioned fields –

the preserve of the paying angler,
or where the molecules were churned,
compressed into channelled energy.

But worst of all was where memories
bubbled up like sulphide in a
beaker. We did not stay there long.

2

At last we reached a rocky height
patrolled by hooded crows and combed
by high breezes. There the river

welled out from a crack onto soft moss.
We found the nub at which chance
and the line of least resistance

had preferred one slope to another.
It was no hard task then to divert
the river's running monologue.

Taking spades and pickaxe, we dipped
our hands into the cresting cold,
created a moment's free fall,

a fanning over a different hill –
then the fan snapped shut, flicked a quick
silver whiplash on the landscape.

We watched it hurdle the contours
to where the mother river glittered
like bubbled glass in the distance.

The stream that we had chaperoned
ebbed in tandem, leaving a valley
sucked in like a toothless mouth.

3

Returning, we passed tongues of slurry
now folding back onto the land.
In concrete towers, wheels had stopped

turning. Men in blue uniforms
held up their hands, while anglers
stared at unsuspected riverscapes.

Further on punts rocked on the dribbles
left by a tide race of debris;
and under now redundant bridges

silted with the history of dead
industries, lost cargoes of people,
the channel oozed like molten tar.

We knew it would not take them long
to find us out – and already
dry bed was becoming veined again

with wet. But we took comfort in how
a force applied to the right place
can change the course of what seems fixed.

Irvine Welsh

WHERE THE DEBRIS MEETS THE SEA

The house in Santa Monica sat tastefully back from Palisades Beach Road, the town's bustling ocean boulevard. This was the top end of the town, its opulence serving as the height to aspire to for the yuppie dwellers of the condominiums further down the Pacific coast. It was a two floored Spanish-style dwelling, partly obscured from the road by a huge stone wall and a range of indigenous American and imported trees. A few yards inside the wall, an electrified security fence ran around the perimeter of the property. Discreetly inside the gate at the entrance to the grounds, a portable cabin was tucked, and outside it sat a burly guard with mirror lens shades.

Wealth was certainly the overall impression given by the property. Unlike nearby Beverly Hills, however, the concept of wealth here seemed more utilitarian, rather than concerned with status. The impression was that wealth was here to be consumed, rather than flaunted ostentatiously for the purpose of inducing respect, awe or envy.

The pool at the back of the house had been drained; this was not a home that was occupied all the year round. Inside, the house was expensively furnished, yet in a stark, practical style.

Four women relaxed in a large room which led, through patio doors, to the dry pool. They were at ease, lounging around silently. The only sounds came from the television, which one of them was watching, and the soft hissing of the air-conditioning which pumped cool, dry air into the house.

A pile of glossy magazines lay on a large black coffee table. They bore such titles as *Wideo*, *Scheme Scene* and *Bevvy Merchants*. Madonna flicked idly through the magazine called *Radge*, coming to an abrupt halt as her eyes feasted on the pallid figure of Deek Prentice, resplendent in a purple, aqua and black shell-suit.

'Phoah! Ah'd shag the erse oafay that anywey,' she lustily exclaimed, breaking the silence, and thrusting the picture under Kylie Minogue's nose.

Kylie inspected the image clinically, 'Hmm... ah dunno... No bad erse oan it like, bit ah'm no really intae flat-toaps.

Still, ah widnae kick it oot ay bed, likes ay, ken?'

'Whae's that?' Victoria Principal asked, filing her nails as she reclined on the couch.

'Deek Prentice fi Gilmerton. Used tae be in the casuals, bit ehs no intae that anymair,' Madonna said, popping a piece of chewing gum into her mouth.

Victoria was enthusiastic. 'Total fuckin ride. Ah bet eh's hung like a hoarse. Like that photae ah goat ay Tam McKenzie, ken fi the Young Leith Team, original seventies line-up. Fuckin welt oan it, man, ah'm telling ye. Phoah, ya cunt ye! Even through the shell-suit, ye kin see ehs tackle bulgin oot. At thoat, fuck me, ah'd gie ma eye teeth tae get ma gums aroond that.'

'Ye'd probably huv tae, if ehzis big is ye say!' smirked Kylie. They all laughed loudly, except Kim Basinger, who sat curled up in a chair watching the television.

'Wishful thinkin gits ye naewhaire,' she mused. Kim was studying the sensual image of Dode Chalmers; bold shaved head, *Castlemaine Four X* t-shirt and Levis. Although Rocky, his faithful American pit-bull terrier was not visible on the screen, Kim noted that his leather and chain leash was bound around Dode's strong, tattooed arm. The eroticism of that image was intense. She wished that she'd video-taped this pro-gramme.

The camera swung over to Rocky, whom Dode described to the interviewer as: 'My one faithful friend in life. We have an uncanny telepathy which goes beyond the archetypal man-beast relationship... in a real sense Rocky is an extension of myself.'

Kim found this a bit pretentious. Certainly, there was little doubt that Rocky was an integral part of the Dode Chalmers legend. They went everywhere together. Kim cynically won-dered, however, just how much of this was a dubious gimmick, manufactured perhaps, by public relations people.

'Fuck...' gasped Kylie, open mouthed. '...what ah'd gie tae be in that dug's position now. Wearin a collar, chained tae Dode's airm. That wid dae me fine.'

'Some fuckin chance,' Kim laughed, more derisively than she'd intended.

Madonna looked across at her. 'Awright then smart cunt. Dinae you be sae fuckin smug,' she said challengingly.

'Aye Kim, dinae tell ays ye widnae git intae his keks if ye

hud the chance,' Victoria sneered.

'That's whit ah sais, bit. Ah'm no gaunny git the chance, so whit good's it talkin aboot it, likesay? Ah'm in here in Southern California n Dode's ower in fuckin Leith.'

They fell into a silence, and watched Dode being interviewed on *The Jimmy McGilvary Show*. Kim thought that McGilvary was a pain in the arse, who seemed to feel that he was as big a star as his guests. He was asking Dode about his love-life.

'In all honesty, I don't have time for heavy relationships at the moment. Right now I'm only interested in all the overtime I can get. After all, one has to remember that trades fortnight isn't that far away,' Dode explained, slightly flushed, but his thin mouth almost curling in a smile.

'Ah'd cowp it,' Kylie licked her bottom lip.

'In a fuckin minute,' Victoria nodded severely, eyes widened.

Madonna was more interested in Deek Prentice. She turned her attention back to the article and continued reading. She was hoping to read something about Deek's split from the casuals. The full story had not come out about that one, and it would be interesting to hear Deek's side of things.

there is hope for us all yet, as Deek is keeping an open mind on romance since his much publicised split with sexy cinema usherette, Sandra Riley. It's obviously an issue where Deek is keen to set the record straight.

'I suppose, in a way, we loved each other too much. There's certainly no hard feelings or bitterness on either side. In fact, I was talking to Sandra on the phone only the other night, so we're still the best of friends. Our respective careers made it difficult to see as much of each other as we would have liked. Obviously cinema isn't a nine to five thing, and furniture removals can take me all over the country, with overnight stays. We got used to not being together, and sort of drifted apart. Unfortunately, it's the nature of the business we're in. Relationships are difficult to sustain.'

Deek's social life is another area where he feels that he has had more than his share of unwelcome publicity. While he makes no secret of an enjoyment of the high life, he feels that 'certain parties' have somewhat exaggerated things.

'So I enjoy the odd game of pool with Dode Chalmers
and Cha Telfer. All I can say is: guilty as charged. Yes, I'm
in the habit of visiting places like the Spey Lounge,
Swanneys and the Clan Tavern; and I enjoy a few pints of
lager. However, the public only see the glamorous side. It's
not as if I'm swilling away every night. Most evenings I'm
home, watching Coronation Street and East Enders. Just
to illustrate how the press get hold of nonsense, a report
appeared in a Sunday newspaper, which shall be nameless,
stating that I was involved in an altercation at a stag night
in Fox's Bar. It's not a boozer I use, and in any case I was
working overtime that night! If I was in the pub as often
as certain gossip columnists claim, I'd hardly be able to
hold down my driving job with Northern Removals. With
three million people unemployed, I've certainly no intention of resting on my laurels.'*

Deek's boss, the experienced supervisor Rab Logan,
agrees. Rab probably knows Deek better than anyone in
the business, and Deek unreservedly credits the dour
Leither with saving his career. Rab told us: 'Deek came to
us with a reputation for being, should we say, somewhat
difficult. He's very much an individual, rather than a team
man, and tended to go off to the pub whenever it took his
fancy. Obviously, with a flit to complete, this lack of
application caused some bad feeling with the rest of the
team. We crossed swords for the first and last time, and
since then, Deek's been a joy to work with. I can't speak
highly enough of him.'*

Deek is only too willing to acknowledge his debt to the
removal Svengali.*

'I owe it all to Rab. He took me aside and told me that
I had what it took to make it in the removals game. The
choice was mine. At the time I was arrogant, and nobody
could tell me anything. However, I remember that excep-
tionally grim and lonely journey home on the number six
bus that day Rab told me a few home truths. He has a
habit of stating the transparently obvious, when you're so
close to it, you can't see the woods for the trees. After a
dressing down from Rab Logan, one tends to shape up.
The lesson I learned from Rab that day was an important
one. In a sense, the removal business is like any other. The

bottom line is, you're only as good as your last flit.'

What Deek eventually wants however, is the opportunity to

'Thirs nought tae stoap us gaun tae Leith, fir a hoaliday n that,' Victoria suggested, tearing Madonna's attention from the magazine.

'Hoaliday… hoaliday…' Madonna sang.

'Aye! We could go tae the *Clan*,' Kylie enthused. 'Imagine the cock in thaire. Comin oot the fuckin waws.' She screwed up her eyes, puckered her lips and blew hard, shaking her head from side to side.

'Ye'd nivir git served in thaire,' Kim sniffed.

'Ken your problem Kim? Ye nivir think fuckin positively enough. We've goat the poppy. Dinae you sit thaire n tell ays you've no goat the hireys,' Madonna remonstrated.

'Ah nivir sais that. It's no jist aboot poppy…'

'Well then. We could go tae Leith. Huv a fuckin barry time. Hoaliday ay a lifetime,' Madonna told her then continued her singing. 'It wid be, it wid be so nice, hoaliday…'

Victoria and Kylie nodded enthusiastically in agreement. Kim looked unconvinced.

'You cunts crack ays up.' She shook her head. 'No fuckin real.'

'Whit's wrong wi your fuckin pus, ya stroppy cunt?' Madonna mouthed belligerently, sitting up in the chair. 'Ye git oan ma fuckin tits Kim, so ye do.'

'We'll nivir go tae fuckin Leith!' Kim said, in a tone of scornful dismissal. 'Youse ur fuckin dreamin.'

'Wi might go one time!' said Kylie, with just a hint of desperation in her voice. The others nodded in agreement.

But in their hearts of hearts, they knew that Kim was right.

Fiona Wilson

SEA MAID

naked I was netted
secured brought ashore
coughing and puking the human
as my old self   that carcass
stripped was stuffed
up the chimney   *integrity?*
I had not thought of it
before your resin
slicked my lips   struck
roots for land   before cradles
and children   before
from all the hidden places came
furious stink of saltwater   and thought
these woman's hands   use them
and reaching beyond cold tiles
in darkness   I felt   skin
its sudden bristle

Maggie York

THE BLANKET & THE WIDOW

Wind me around your legs
spill soup and tomato seeds over
my darned patches.
Feed me.

 I don't have time for cold weather
 cruises and dressing for dinner and
 being polite to lilac blondes
 in elegant greys.
 Leave me be.

I could make you dream
smell his hands, his morning armpits
hear the movement of his hungover bowels:
I can resurrect your sex life.
Trust me.

 You accuse me of desertion and failure.
 I hope you mould into the last box
 for Oxfam; never to be chosen.
 Leave me be.

Pick me up off this chair, his death bed
I want to live again, I need to breathe.
I could ease life into you.
Save me.

 His shadow lies askew in your folds.
 Leave me be.